SEE TO PLAY

# SEE *to* PLAY
## THE EYES OF ELITE ATHLETES

MICHAEL A. PETERS, OD

BASCOM HILL PUBLISHING GROUP

Copyright © 2012 by Michael A. Peters, OD.

Bascom Hill Publishing Group
212 3ʳᵈ Avenue North, Suite 290
Minneapolis, MN 55401
612.455.2293
www.bascomhillbooks.com

ISBN-13: 978-1-938008-00-9
LCCN: 2011945645

Distributed by Itasca Books

Cover Design by Alan Pranke
Typeset by Madge Duffy

*Printed in the United States of America*

*This book is dedicated to:*
*Stacey, Kelsie, Carson, Kerrigan,*
*Walbert, Becky, David, and Adam*

# CONTENTS

# INTRODUCTION

*Happy Man: Welcome to Hollywood! What's your dream? Everybody comes here; this is Hollywood, land of dreams. Some dreams come true, some don't; but keep on dreamin'—this is Hollywood. Always time to dream, so keep on dreamin'.*
—last line from the movie *Pretty Woman*

What was my dream? I wanted to be a professional football player. I know that the dream didn't start at birth, but I can't remember a time when I didn't have it.

By my senior year of high school, I was in great physical shape and had developed a portfolio of good stats. I was six feet tall and weighed 215 pounds. I could run a 4.4-second 40-yard dash. My bench press was over 400 pounds. I had rushed over 1,000 yards per season for my three years at the varsity level and played both offense and defense. In track, I qualified for and participated in the state track meet each of my four years in high school in several different running events. I had both speed and strength.

However, instead of achieving my dream, I ended up as a statistic, one of the 94 percent of high school seniors who don't make the jump from high school football to the NCAA. The reason was quite simple: I couldn't see to play. I was nearsighted. I had no control over my vision when playing. I'm sure I wasn't the only kid out there playing sports in a fuzzy world, but there weren't many options in the 1960s and '70s for us blurry-eyed athletes. I couldn't see with the soft contact lenses that I tried to wear because they didn't fit optimally for sports (the size that I needed to fit the shape of my eyes wasn't developed until a few years after my football career ended), and the hard contact lenses were so uncomfortable they felt like bricks in my eyes. I could see with glasses, but they didn't fit in my football helmet very well. Besides, their design didn't allow for much air flow, which caused them to fog up like crazy when my core temperature got to competition level. So once the game started, I couldn't even see *with* the glasses.

My contact lenses were not dependable and my glasses were too annoying, so I usually chose to play without correction and, as one would expect, everything was blurry. But I really wanted to play football at the next level after high school, and I made the decision to walk on to the football program at West Virginia University. So I showed up—me, my one pair of soft contact lenses that didn't fit exactly right, my one set of ugly black glasses that also didn't fit right, and my athletic talents.

The first day of practice was a big day, so I decided to wear my contacts. *Boom!* The football just appeared in my hands out of nowhere. It was traveling at least 70 mph, thrown by the arm of Jeff Hostetler, who had just transferred to WVU from Penn State. I was there. My hands were there. But my left contact lens was somewhere up underneath my left eyelid, and my right contact decided to dry out in my eye at that very instant.

I pretty much kept having the same experience in varying forms, and the tasks of the practice days began becoming bigger struggles. I was performing at the right levels in all the physical tasks—running, cutting, reading cuts, blocking, and strength— but I couldn't reliably catch the ball. It started creeping into my head, a crack in my mental armor. I was doing well in all the running drills. I was doing great in the workouts. But when I went out for a pass, it was a different story. I knew I couldn't really keep up visually, and it began to affect me mentally.

I needed to make a decision, and I ended up taking a break from football for a semester, hoping to get better control of my eyes and walk on again in the spring. In the meantime, I would figure out my class schedule and focus on academics.

One of the fortunate things that I started to do early in high school (due to the prodding of my parents) was think of other professions that I could go into if football didn't pan out for me. Because my physical ability was affected by my decreased visual ability, being able to "see to play" consumed so much of my thinking that I thought of becoming an eye doctor who specialized in the unique visual demands of athletes.

When looking at the two types of eye doctors that I could become, I felt optometry suited me better than ophthalmology. Ophthalmology mainly deals with eye surgery. Optometry deals more with checking eyes, prescribing glasses and contacts, and using vision therapy to help fine-tune eye muscles and the visual system. Optometry was also a field with which I was very familiar because of my experience as a patient. I had been into an eye doctor's office often and was familiar with the process of having an eye exam. I knew about wearing eyeglasses and contact lenses. I began contacting several optometry schools to find out what steps were necessary to become an eye doctor.

The decision to temporarily set aside my cleats my freshman year ended up being the end of my football career. The frustration that I felt helped fuel my drive as I started my quest to become an eye doctor. I strengthened my resolve to become an eye doctor who specialized in helping athletes with their vision.

After my undergraduate work, I went to the Pennsylvania College of Optometry in Philadelphia. Philadelphia is a great sports town. My friends and I took in most of the sports venues. We got to see Julius "Dr. J" Erving play with the Sixers. We saw a lot of Major League Baseball by going to Phillies games. We took in NFL games by watching the Eagles, and I was introduced to the NHL by cheering on the Philadelphia Flyers.

My dream of becoming a professional football player was in full transition to a new dream of becoming an eye doctor who helped athletes succeed at the highest levels in their sport. I didn't want to limit myself to one sport and developed the desire to learn the visual aspects of all sports. I didn't want players to be weeded out by their eyes like I had been. I wanted to help them make it. And, most importantly, I developed the drive to help them reach their genetic potentials by helping them perfect their visual systems. I wanted to help them become elite and, in my opinion, the best way to achieve this was by learning how the best athletes used their visual systems and then giving this information to those who dreamed of becoming the best.

In 1988 I decided to settle in Raleigh, North Carolina, a hotbed of sports activity. I met my future business partner, Stephen Bolick, OD, and became a partner in the business he founded, Eye Care Associates. This was already one of the premier contact-lens practices in the nation, and I became proficient in fitting the most advanced contact lenses. I also became the director of our sports-vision program. Eye Care Associates is currently the twentieth-largest provider of eye care in the United States with 30 doctors and 20 offices.

I am living the dream and loving every minute of it! I have helped correct the visual problems of athletes from grade school to the professional level. I've helped collegiate athletes in many types of sports see, and I've also directed the sports-vision branch of an entire collegiate program. I've taken care of the visual needs of Olympians. I've provided care for professional football players who have made it to the playoff levels in the National Football League, played in Pro Bowls, and won a Super Bowl. I've cared for athletes who have gone on to play basketball at the professional level. I've been the eye-care provider of professional baseball players—including one MVP—who have been on World Series Championship teams and All-Star teams. I've provided eye care for professional hockey players who have won the Stanley Cup, played on All-Star teams, and made it to the Hall of Fame. I have worked with professional soccer players and professional golfers.

I know athletes, and I know athletes' eyes. I know how the vision system works, and I know how it needs to work in order to be the best.

I am living the dream! And I am still dreaming by helping athletes **see to play**!

# CHAPTER 1
## ONLY THE BEST EYES MAKE IT

You've got to see to play. Elite athletes do.

Elite athletes are better than average athletes. They've taken the physical edge that they were given genetically, spent countless hours training and conditioning, and honed their skills to reach the highest level. They've left no stone unturned in their quest to be the best. They can run faster, skate faster, swim faster, jump higher, and throw a ball farther, faster, and more accurately. They're stronger, and their bodies have higher endurance levels.

Elite athletes also have superior vision compared to other athletes. They see better. Their vision is clearer. Their peripheral vision is wider. Their eye muscles move better. Their depth perception is better. They have an ability to change focus faster. Their eye-hand and eye-hand-body coordination is better. Their mind's eye is more intuitive. They stay focused better. Their anticipation is better. They can see to play at the highest level.

While reading an article in one of my optometric journals a few years ago, this notion really hit me. The article broke down the percentage of people in the United States, by age group, who require vision correction in order to achieve their best vision. It stated that 59 percent of 18- to 34-year-olds need some type of prescription to correct their vision. Since the majority of professional athletes fall into this age group, it should follow that 59 percent of them should also have some type of vision correction in order for them to see to play.

1

I started to think back to my work with professional athletes. This percentage didn't seem correct to me as it translated to their world. Considering the 20 years that I had worked with professional athletes, I would have estimated that the percentage who needed glasses, contacts, or surgery in order to see to play was considerably less than 59 percent, probably closer to 30 percent.

I decided the best way to determine the true percentage for athletes competing at the highest level was to poll professional sports teams to find out how many of their athletes actually needed glasses or contacts or had had refractive surgery.

I sent a questionnaire about their athletes' vision to all of the trainers working for the National Football League (NFL), National Basketball Association (NBA), and Major League Baseball (MLB) in the 2009–2010 seasons. To represent the National Hockey League (NHL), I used my own data from the 14 years I have spent working with the Carolina Hurricanes.

The results were as follows in terms of what percentage of players needed visual assistance:

- 17.1 percent of NFL players
- 16 percent of NBA players
- 29.6 percent of MLB players
- 20.2 percent of NHL players

The average was even lower than I had thought it would be. Across all four of these sports, the average was actually around 21 percent. I realized that the eyes of professional athletes are substantially better than the eyes of the average population in the same age group. You really do have to see to play.

And that got me thinking some more. Where do the rest of those athletes who need vision correction go on their way to reaching elite status? Could it be that a full 38 percent of the people in this age group, the rest of the ones who need vision correction, get weeded out of their sport because of their eyes? Are there really that many people who may miss out on their lifelong dream of becoming professional athletes because of poor vision?

Again, my experience as an eye doctor working with professional athletes told me that wearing a prescription couldn't be the whole story. I imagined that there had to be other traits of the visual system that contributed to holding athletes back. This helped fuel my drive to search for those other reasons and ultimately help athletes succeed.

I've had the good fortune to work with trainers, coaches, and people in the sports-medicine community who are very forward-thinking in their approaches when it comes to helping athletes compete at the highest level. One such person is Peter Friesen, the head trainer of the NHL's Carolina Hurricanes. He pushes everyone to be the best, and that attitude has helped push me to improve my sports-vision specialty. He has helped me to better understand the physical demands placed on athletes in motion.

I have been able to take what I know about the vision system, integrate how vision translates into sport-specific tasks, and develop techniques that help athletes achieve their best visual performances. Working together, Peter and I have taken his approach to physical training and incorporated vision training to improve athletes' flexibility, range of motion, and general physical/mental/eye-body-mind preparation. I believe that he is one of the top trainers to integrate vision training with physical training and one of the few who understands how vision can lead the body.

I asked Peter if he would write his views about vision in

sports as it relates to professional athletes and other athletes he has trained. Here is what he wrote:

*As I look at all the trends in sports medicine and how things are constantly changing to improve the athlete's performance, one aspect stands alone as the most underrated attribute an athlete can develop. Without question, in my 30 years as a physical therapist, athletic trainer, and strength coach, I have found that we underestimate the importance of vision and vision training.*

*I feel lucky that I have developed a long and strong relationship with Mike Peters, our team optometrist for the last 14 years. Through his instruction and guidance, we have worked hard to incorporate vision training into our high-performance training.*

*To realize just how important vision is, try testing athletes' muscles with the athletes looking at their own muscle and then again with them looking away. They will immediately notice an improvement in strength. Another quick test is to have athletes evaluate their vertical jump with a downward gaze versus an upward gaze. The upward gaze adds a minimum of two inches to their vertical height. The old adage that the eyes drive the body is very appropriate for these two tests.*

*The subject of eyes is in every aspect of my sports-medicine program. It starts at the NHL combines, where results of the sports-vision scores are taken under serious consideration during the NHL Draft. It has been shown that the single-best fitness score that correlates to the chances of making the NHL are results from the combine vision tests. At our summer conditioning camp, young players get their first exposure to Dr. Peters and his more in-depth vision testing and exercises to improve and develop overall high-performance vision. In addition, there is a significant section in the dry-land manual on vision exercises, which we expect athletes to follow in the summer months.*

*During preseason testing, eye scores are again scrutinized by management and coaching staff. It is almost always a certainty that our best goaltenders and best face-off athletes score the highest.*

*Another area in which we utilize eye scores is when making sure an athlete's vision is back to normal after suffering a concussion. I believe this is a critical area to which we often don't devote enough attention. We generally look at many other signs and symptoms but fall short when it comes to making sure the vision is back to normal. This then may put the athlete in harm's way and at risk of another injury or exacerbating the present symptoms, thus setting back the athlete.*

Over the years, my work with Pete and with other members of the amateur and professional sports communities has helped me pursue my goal: giving those kids who might have gotten weeded out because of vision problems a fighting chance to make it to the top. I want to make sure that those athletes don't get lost climbing up their sports' ladders by equipping them with tools to stay on the path of success visually. And I also want to help those athletes who don't need corrective aids, like glasses or contact lenses, reach their genetic potentials and push their games to higher levels by maximizing all of their visual traits.

By writing this book, I want to provide the parents of child athletes, the trainers and coaches who work with athletes, and athletes at every level another weapon in their arsenal to help them become the best.

- Parents, if you wear glasses or contacts, you'd better be on vision alert if your child dreams of becoming a professional athlete someday, as the general thinking is that many vision problems are hereditary. Even if you're a parent who has naturally great vision, you need to be on alert as well. While the concept of blurred vision might be new to you, your child athlete may fall victim to the general shift to nearsightedness across the entire population that is blamed on the increased use of computers, video games, digital screens, and books. In a 30-year span, the United States has seen its population become 66 percent more nearsighted.

- Trainers and coaches, if you want to help your athletes maintain the highest competitive level and even make it to the pros, you should be constantly talking to them about their vision and pushing them to be diligent about improving their visual systems.

- Athletes, if you want to be the best, you'd better pay attention to how well you see by getting your vision tested frequently and also by training your visual system to make sure you've done everything possible to perform at your genetic potential.

Many of you understand the physical side of athletics because you're in a sport or have played one. You understand how the body functions while playing, how the body is tested for physical fitness, and how the body is trained for peak performance. For many of us, vision is the last thing we think about in athletics. (I often hear comments like, "I can see just fine. I can see the ball. I don't need any help! I've gotten to this level, and I'm doing great!") So I will give you an example that uses your understanding of how athletes are assessed on the physical aspects of the game and then translate it to the eye world.

Let's first look at how the body is evaluated in athletics. The NFL Combine Timing and Testing Sessions are a good example of a complete physical evaluation. Football players have to go through these drills before being drafted by an NFL team. The sessions give the teams a system to rate how athletes perform and a tool for comparing athletes to each other (besides just using stats from their performance in high school and college games). The sessions give teams ways to compare athletes with each other before deciding which players to draft.

The body is broken down into parts and tested for a better understanding of how these athletes tick. The tests and evaluations include a physical exam to record physical attributes and also each athlete's performance in the 40-yard dash, bench press, vertical jump, broad jump, 20-yard shuttle, three-cone drill, and 60-yard shuttle. Then the players perform position-specific drills. The drills are timed and recorded on video so that the coaches can break down every aspect of how the players performed and use this information to compare and rank each athlete's performance.

In the same way that the NFL uses this comprehensive method for ranking athletes, I have broken down the visual system into its important parts, and I test and rank athletes using each of these traits. I developed this method to compare the athletes who are on the Carolina Hurricanes by position. They are measured for acuity, peripheral vision, eye alignment, eye-muscle movement, eye-muscle strength, depth perception, eye focusing, and visual memory. These findings are scored to help determine which players have the overall best visual systems; I then rank them accordingly from first to last by the positions they play and produce an overall team ranking.

This ranking method lets us know how the elite athlete's visual system works. It gives the team a tool to predict which of the younger players may develop into better athletes based on whether they have the visual traits of the elite. In this book,

I will describe the different parts of the visual system that I use in my ranking method and give you a better understanding of each one.

In our practices at Eye Care Associates in North Carolina, my partner Stephen Bolick, OD, and associates Jason Price, OD, and Monica Reeves, OD, helped me develop our High Performance Vision program. This program tests these basic parts of the visual system and designs personal training programs to help athletes reach their peak genetic potential. We provide this care in three phases. In the first phase, we use the latest testing technology to evaluate the visual system and, if needed, fit the most advanced contact lenses and sports eyewear available. Our second phase incorporates the use of vision therapy and vision training to help athletes enhance how their eyes see and work and improve eye-hand, eye-hand-body, and eye-mind coordination and mental preparation. Our third phase advances to the ultimate level of integrating these vision exercises with core training. These exercises are performed in our facilities, and athletes are given additional exercises to work on at home. (Visit our website at www.ecanc.com to learn more about High Performance Vision.)

Vision is important in all sports, and important decisions are made using information about an athlete's vision. In 1999 the Tampa Bay Rays had the first draft pick in the MLB Draft. That first pick is important, because the first player drafted commands the most money, at the highest cost to the team that makes it. So while the team is hoping to pick the next Babe Ruth, they are also worried that their pick may become an expensive bust. The Rays were contemplating using their first pick on Josh Hamilton, a high school senior from Raleigh. I was the eye doctor for their AAA squad, the Durham Bulls, and they sent

Josh to me to have his eyes checked. By testing his vision, the Rays were trying to leave no stone unturned. As Josh reported to the local newspaper, it turned out that his vision was 20/10, which has been the must-have in baseball since the days of Ted Williams.

I remember talking with Josh and the people with him after his eye exam. I asked, "Can you believe that in one week you're going to be a millionaire?" He did end up being the first player drafted that next week and received a $3 million signing bonus. He has since been in the MLB All-Star Game, broke a record in the 2008 Home Run Derby, played in the postseason, and in 2010 was named the most valuable player in the American League. (He's also a local boy, and I recommend that you read his book, *Beyond Belief: Finding the Strength to Come Back*.)

Speaking of Josh, I think this would be a good time to describe what I consider to be the definition of an *elite athlete*, so that you and I are on the same page. I've worked with elite athletes who have made it to the NFL, NBA, MLB, NHL, PGA, LPGA, professional soccer, and the Olympics. I've also tested athletes who have made it to the All-Star level in their respective sports and who are champions from Super Bowl, World Series, and Stanley Cup teams. I also consider athletes who have gone on to excel in their sports individually, as noted by their high statistics, to be elite. I think we can agree that these groups of athletes are the best of the best. I use the vision and visual traits of the elite athletes with whom I have worked as the high bar for all athletes to achieve.

The group of elite athletes we just defined represents a very small number of athletes others try to emulate.

To be honest with you, I wish we could consider athletes who make the jump from high school to college athletics elite (but we can't because we know that their ultimate goal is to be a member of the group we just defined). Have you seen the statistics on that? Let me break down the percentages of high school senior athletes who make the jump to the college level and the percentages of high school senior athletes who make it to the professional level.

**Football**:
- 1 out of 17 plays in college (5.8 percent)
- 8 out of 10,000 make it to the NFL (0.08 percent)

**Basketball**:
- Less than 1 out of 35 plays in college (2.9 percent)
- 3 out of 10,000 make it to the NBA (0.03 percent)

(The percentages are pretty much the same for men and women.)

**Baseball**:
- 3 out of 50 play in college (6 percent)
- 1 out of 200 makes it to the MLB level (0.44 percent)

**Hockey**:
- 11 out of 100 play in college (11 percent)
- 1 out of 300 makes it to the NHL (0.32 percent)

**Soccer**:
- 3 out of 50 play in college (6 percent)
- 1 out of 1,250 makes it to the MLS level (0.07 percent)

Even if we can't include college athletes in our definition of *elite athletes*, the chance of making the jump from the high school level to the college level is pretty small, which means you'd better get cracking at an early age if you want to make it. The NCAA made a rule in 2009 that colleges could recruit male basketball athletes in the seventh grade. That's pretty wild, isn't it? Eventually this act of recruiting the very young may move into other sports. Think about that!

Seventh graders are around 12 years old. Parents of a 12-year-old playing a sport and hoping to succeed at the college level had better hope he's developed his game. I guess that makes the fifth grade, or the age of 10, a pretty important year for the child to begin to stand out from the other athletes. Parents of these athletes will definitely want him working on eye-hand coordination even a few years earlier, say around seven. There are many exercises discussed in Chapter 11 that athletes can begin at a young age that just may help more quickly develop their eye-hand coordination.

Parents of an athlete working on his eye-hand coordination at such a young age will want to make sure he sees well and should get him a professional eye examination by the age of six. Later on in this book I recommend children get their eyes checked by an eye doctor at around the age of two if their parents are considering them for a lifetime of sports.

Most people think that having their child's vision tested at school or at a pediatrician's or doctor's office during a routine physical is all of the vision testing required for young athletes. This is not true. In addition to the visual problems that an eye-chart test can uncover, there are several other areas of vision that can contribute to or interfere with the success of an athlete. Small deficiencies in one of these areas will probably not be noticed at the school or in the doctor's office, but at some point they may cause the athlete to hit the glass ceiling in his or her sport. Identifying and correcting these problems early with an optometrist will help ensure that the athlete can reach his or her full potential.

I've often heard parents of 9- and 10-year-old athletes who I've told need glasses say, "He's doing great right now! He's one of the best players on his team. We'll worry about it later when it bothers him. Plus, he probably won't wear them anyway. Ha, ha, ha." But parents, the point is: don't you want to help him be the best that he can be? That starts right now, not later when your child is having problems advancing in his sport.

I have found that many athletes get bogged down by their vision problems when they reach their senior year in high school and can't make the jump to college athletics. I've even seen several players in AAA baseball who haven't been able to make the jump to the major leagues, and one of the contributing issues is that their vision is slightly off and hard to correct.

Athletes who want to become elite athletes have to try to fix all the weak parts of their bodies and games to excel in their sports, and the eyes are one of the biggest keys to success. Sure, Johnny's doing well at 10, and Sally's doing well at 12, but Johnny actually could be doing a lot better if he worked to get his eye muscles moving better, and Sally could improve if she used that minor glasses correction that she needs to help her see her best so that her eye-hand-body coordination can fully develop. I can assure you that by the time athletes make it to the professional level, they get serious about even the smallest visual issues.

Before discussing all of the different aspects of how elite athletes use their vision, I want to first go over some of the basics of vision, the brain, and the body. I think it will help better illustrate how all these systems are integrated. Elite athletes seem to have all of these systems finely tuned and humming together: body, soul, and mind in perfect harmony. The proverb tells us that the eyes are the windows to the soul. But the eyes are much more than that, as the visual system feeds into the body's other systems.

The eyes take in information about what is going on around

us and feed the information into the brain. The brain digests the information and then makes a determination about whether or not to act on the information. If the decision is to act on the information, the brain sends out impulses so that we move the muscles that are required to make the correct movements (as in hitting a baseball: when the ball is pitched, the hitter's body must move in a correct and consecutive manner). Or, the brain may decide that a particular move is a fakeout and react accordingly.

I use a drill for running backs in the NFL combine as an illustration of the eyes leading the body. It's called the off-tackle reaction drill. The running back starts off from a standing two-point position. A coach hands him the football, and he has to accelerate in a straight line for about 10 yards. In the middle of this path are four bags placed about a yard apart that the athlete must run over while keeping his vision straight ahead, focused on a coach holding another bag. As the player nears the end of this path, the coach moves the bag he is holding to the left or right, and the athlete has to turn 90 degrees to the opposite direction, sprint another 10 yards or so around a cone, and turn again in order to sprint down to the end of the course. The body has to continue working in perfect motion over the bags and around the cones as the eyes get the information about which direction the runner must turn. The brain has to make a correct decision in a split second and move the body accordingly. Players are ranked on how fast and how well they perform this task, which ultimately boils down to a correct visual decision.

The visual pathway is one of the major contributors of information to the brain. I've seen claims that 80 percent of perceptual input for sports is visual. This is one of the big reasons why our eyes can also trick us. They give us a lot of information, and sometimes it's too much! I call this *visual noise* and have devoted Chapter 7 to the topic. How does the old saying go? "Believe only half of what you see and nothing that you hear." With the importance that the brain gives to the eyes for input, it only makes sense that we jump deep into the visual system, make sure it's working right, and make any necessary corrections that could aid an athlete in reaching his or her fullest potential.

Do vision exercises improve sports performance? I do believe that vision exercises can benefit athletic performance. In this book, I'm writing about my specific findings and experiences. I include exercises that athletes who I have worked with have found beneficial and use today, and I also include my views on how these exercises help athletes reach their genetic potential.

I've also read articles by other eye doctors who believe that eye exercises help athletes perform better. And I've read articles in which athletes themselves—including the likes of Jim Harbaugh, George Brett, Michael Campbell, Nick Faldo, Larry Fitzgerald Jr., Lou Piniella, and Michelle Wie—have spoken out about how they benefited from eye exercises.

I hope this book will introduce people to the visual tools needed to get athletes performing at a peak level. I want to help get everyone versed on how the visual system works and how important it is to make sure it's working properly. This book will also provide a better understanding on how athletes use their vision in sports. I've tried to keep it simple and fun so that athletes, parents, trainers, coaches, and doctors can take what they learn and put it into action. I will break down the different parts of the visual system, how they work, how they should work, and how they work in elite athletes as well as describing exercises

SEE TO PLAY                    15

that can make one's visual system better. I'll throw in a couple of stories about athletes with whom I've worked in the past to illustrate these points.

Throughout the book, the most important concepts are highlighted as *See to Play Tips*. I have found these tips to be the most important tricks of the trade in the world of sports vision. These are the basics on how the eyes can affect an athlete's game. There is science behind some of the tips, and others are meant to be more general rules of thumb. As an eye doctor actively involved in High Performance Vision, I've used these tips daily while working with athletes over the past 20 years.

For the most up-to-date information on how to see to play, visit my website at www.seetoplay.com.

# CHAPTER 2
## SUPERHUMAN ACUITY

Visual acuity is the essential building block of an athlete's vision. You have probably heard these terms: 20/20, 20/30, 20/10, and so on. They describe how well a person sees, which is known as "visual acuity." Elite athletes have better visual acuity, especially in sports that are visually demanding. (By "visually demanding," I mean that a baseball player or hockey player has a harder task visually than an athlete in a sport such as swimming.) Just as the old adage states that "the cream rises to the top," I've found that the athletes who make it to the top levels in visually demanding sports usually have the best vision.

The best visual acuity of any athlete I've ever tested is 20/8. Eric Staal and Cam Ward of the Carolina Hurricanes are two athletes who have that acuity, and they've allowed me to share their names with you. I've found this level of visual acuity with a few other athletes who I have evaluated, but as you read on, you will find that this is indeed rare.

I asked Eric if there was any part of his vision or visual system that he felt added to his game or helped him be the All-Star hockey player he is. He told me that he couldn't point to one visual trait in particular other than his acuity. He's always had a sense that he could see better than other people. He told me that as a child he could often see something far away that others couldn't. So he would constantly test himself by looking far away and seeing if others could see with the same detail. He knew early on that he had better vision than most, and he still pushes to keep his acuity sharp the way he did as a child. We can rank athletes by their vision. This works in the same way that we compare information on how fast an athlete runs a 40-yard dash, how fast he throws a ball, and how high he can leap vertically. We can collect eye information to rank him visually with his peers. Visual acuity is the first measurement that I use in the ranking system that I developed for my work with athletes and sports teams. Athletes with better visual acuity are ranked higher than those with lesser or average acuity. Acuity isn't the only factor used in my overall ranking method (found in Chapter 13), but it is the first place. It is also the first place where elite athletes start to rule visually.

Do you remember your first experience with high-definition television? I do, clear as day. I sat down on a chair and stared straight ahead. I pushed a button. *BANG! POP!* I was transported to a spot in the middle of a forest. I could see for what appeared to be a mile into the woods. I could see each tree. I could see each leaf. I could almost touch them if I wanted. I felt like I was actually there. I could see a deer off in the distance. He was walking toward me. I could see his majestic 12-point antler rack. I could hear him rustling a few leaves as he walked. I could hear him as he chewed on the foliage. It seemed as though all of my senses were heightened. I could hear the birds that were flying overhead. I could hear the water as it trickled down the stream in the background.

As you can tell by this description, the Discovery Channel was one of the first stations to send its signal out in high-def, and it was the first one that I watched. I can tell you, the difference was amazing! Things in motion appeared clearer, and the moving objects and landscape were not so blurry. Details far off were distinguishable. Normal channels appeared washed out in comparison. It was hard to go back to the old way of viewing television once I knew there was something out there that was different and better. High-def became the new and only way to watch television from that day forward.

Visual acuity is the measure of how well someone sees in detail. Since the time most of us were in grade school, we've looked at the eye chart that starts with the big *E*. We covered one eye with our hand or a patch and were directed to start reading down to the lowest line of letters that we could see. Similarly, many of us have also had to go to the DMV and look in a machine to read the numbers, letters, and symbols that are present as a condition of getting our driver's licenses.

Dr. Hermann Snellen developed this system of measuring acuity in 1862 with the *E* chart that bears his name. This chart can be found in schools and many physicians' offices. The eye-testing community has agreed that it provides an adequate, standard way of evaluating visual acuity.

20/20 is considered to be normal or standard vision. My vision is the standard 20/20. But what about vision that is better than 20/20; what about vision that is superhuman? To help you understand more about superhuman vision, let's compare my standard vision to an athlete who has better than 20/20 vision. The smallest lettering that I can read from 10 feet away, the 20/10 athlete can still read when he is 20 feet away. The smallest lettering that I can see at 15 feet, an athlete with 20/15 vision can see when standing 20 feet away. The 20/10 and 20/15 athletes see better than my 20/20 because they can make out smaller items farther away than I can. In sports, that means they see objects more clearly and before other players.

I'm asked these questions by athletes all the time: What's my vision? Is my vision normal? Is my vision better than average? What athlete has had the best vision that you've ever tested? Can you get me to see that good?

## 20/8...Simply the Best!

20/8 vision requires a next-to-perfect eyeball and is a very rare find. Each time I work with athletes who have 20/8 vision, it strikes me that their eyeballs are just genetically designed better, mainly in two areas:

- The optics of their eyeballs are more exact. A study was published in 2010 that showed that the eyes of professional baseball players focus light better than those of the average person. This study measured the optics of different eyes, including how light enters and reaches the back of the eye to produce clear images. In some eyes, errors known as *aberrations* occur that can make those images blurrier. When the group of professional baseball players was measured, they had superior optical traits and fewer aberrations. This adds to the argument that elite athletes seem to have better eyeballs to help them see to play.
- They have better high-def receptors in their eyes. Visual acuity is determined by cells known as *cones* in an area in the back of the eye, which is called the *macula*. The cones are like the number of pixels in a digital camera, and how many we have and in how large of an area they are found is genetically predetermined for each of us. Elite athletes seem to have more pixels and have a larger area in use to provide this clarity. (This is discussed in depth in Chapter 3.)

I tell people that visual acuity can be looked at like a group of people running a race. You always find about two or three people running out in front of the group. Then, there is the large pack of people running together. All are about the same in the pack; some are in the front of the pack, some are in the middle, and some are in the rear. And then you have the stragglers. Inevitably, two or three are dragging behind, and usually one is way behind. Visual acuity can be looked at the same way: 20/8 is the first person way out in front, and 20/10–20/15 is the next little group. The 20/20 people are running in the front part of the main pack, with 20/25 in the middle and 20/30 at the back of the pack. The stragglers start with the 20/40 crowd and start to drop to 20/50 or 20/60 or 20/100, and so on.

20/8 in this race represents the really rare runner, the runner about whom stories get told. These are the legends. If this runner is in the race, he or she is way out in front of the first two runners. These runners are so gifted they are usually plucked from the normal population and placed in some special training regimen for the Olympics. Their gift is so rare that one has to go to the Olympics or World Games to see this runner.

> **See to Play Tip 1:**
> **See the best; be the best! See first; be first!**

See to Play Tip 1 sounds pretty straightforward, doesn't it? Athletes who can see images clearly earlier and from farther away have a visual jump on the average athlete.

Elite athletes in visually demanding sports or skilled positions see better than average athletes. Many of these athletes also have better physical characteristics as well. They're the ones who, from birth, have the traits to run faster, be stronger, react

quicker, jump higher, and do all other physical things better.
I have worked with some athletes who have less physical stature than their peers (that is, they're smaller and not as strong)
but have developed into elite athletes. It turns out that the overwhelming majority of these athletes have great visual skills. Their
vision has become a major force in bridging the physical gap. Do
I really mean that vision can equalize any physical weaknesses?
Yes, I do. I believe it, because vision starts the body in sports.
Vision starts eye-hand reactions, it starts the body in motion,
and it begins the athlete's game. The athlete who can see farther
and quicker has a jump-start.

I had an exciting experience with one of the first USA
National baseball teams I examined a few years ago. This is basically the College All-Star team. Young men come from all over
the United States at the beginning of summer to try out for the
team. This team eventually tries to make it to the Olympics. It
was my job to make sure they were seeing as well as they could.

The first gentleman walked into my exam room. He was
20/10. The second guy who came in tested the same at 20/10.
The third guy came in. You guessed it: 20/10. At this point, I
began to get a little nervous. Did I have the right eye chart? Did
I have my test distance set too close?

The fourth guy read the 20/10 line as well. I began remeasur-
ing my test distance. I checked the chart to verify that I had
brought the right one. I checked every aspect of my evaluation
procedure, and everything was proper. When all was said and
done, two of the athletes in this group tested at 20/8, most were
20/10, and a couple of the stragglers were 20/15. That was the
best visual acuity that I had ever seen in one group of athletes.
Collectively, they represented the best group of eyeballs that I
had ever evaluated at one time.

Why haven't I found athletes with vision that is better than 20/8? I learned years ago in school that 20/8 is the best vision physiologically possible. I accepted that as fact. But in this world where running and swimming records are still being broken, couldn't it be possible that human vision is getting better? Sounds reasonable to me, so I've been testing athletes for the next level of visual acuity—which is 20/7—though I still haven't found it. When I do start finding that—and I will eventually—the push will then be to find someone with 20/6 vision.

Athletes are going to have an edge if their eyesight can be corrected to better than 20/20 or if their eyes can work better. I've known several athletes with great uncorrected vision, and I was still able to take them to superhuman vision with just a very mild prescription. They passed the routine vision screening as normal, but they didn't realize that they were actually capable of seeing even better and being superhuman!

Now that athletes' eyes have been tested and they see better than 20/20 without any correction, they probably don't need any further help from the eye doctor, right? The exact opposite is the case: these athletes can quite possibly achieve even better vision with the help of glasses or contacts. Just like a race car's engine is fine-tuned with a higher level of scrutiny than the family car, an athlete's visual acuity should be fine-tuned to the highest level. If this requires the use of a prescription to get a person seeing to his or her highest genetic potential, we refer to this as *best corrected acuity*. Best corrected acuity means just what it suggests: athletes are seeing with 100 percent of their personal acuity, the clearest vision possible for them.

Chris Richard of the Durham Bulls is a great example of this point. He's seen better than average throughout his career, but I found out through testing that I could help him reach a higher level. He wrote the following passage for me to add to this book:

*The Bulls season has been over for a couple of weeks, and I've managed to travel across the country, make a few stops along the way, and end up back home in San Diego. It's a time of the year when guys usually relax and think about what they need to work on to be better next year. . . . Well, for the first time in my career, I'm thinking about my eyes.*

*I've spent the last 12 years playing professional baseball, and it took me this long to realize that I need glasses. Maybe "need" isn't the right word. I have good vision, 20/15, but the left eye is weaker than the right and has an astigmatism that gives me a problem, especially with glare. Since we play the majority of our games at night, the ball most often looks like a streaking comet or a glowing orb instead of a spinning ball with laces. Not a big problem when it's a fastball, but any breaking stuff can cause cries from the stands of, "How can he swing at that!"*

*After so many years of playing, why did it take so long for me to try glasses? Well, it's a combination of having success, thinking glasses couldn't help me that much, and the maturity factor of getting past the stigma of wearing them. Basically the "If it ain't broke, don't try and fix it" approach.*

*Well, I have to thank Richmond for breaking me down and creating the "need." It wasn't until I played at the Diamond, where the lights are horrific, that I surrendered to the fact that I could not see there, that I had no chance. When you reach that point as a player, it's either time to start learning about the insurance business or hope there's something wrong with your eyes. So when I found out the International League Championship had to go through Richmond, I went straight to the optometrist [Dr. Peters at Eye Care Associates] and got some prescription Oakleys.*

*I practiced with them a few times to get used to them, but I was nervous about trying them in a game, so I waited until my second at-bat in Richmond. My first at-bat had gone so poorly—slider in the dirt—that my thoughts, which usually would be searching the "making adjustments" file in my head, were now leaning toward the direction of,* That was the worst at-bat of my life. *I didn't have a clue up there. Walking back to the dugout, I knew I couldn't do any worse, so I was going to make a change.*

*After I dropped my helmet and bat off at the rack, I went into the clubhouse and grabbed my glasses. The glasses went on and, looking in the mirror, I knew I would soon be hearing the nickname "Specs," but it would be worth it. As I walked out to the dugout, I could see my teammates looking at me and thinking,* What is he doing? He's had a good year, hitting .400 in the playoffs, and he picks now to try something new? *With a smile I acknowledged their curiosities and ran out to first base noticing that my digital world had now become high-definition. Everything was bolder and crisper, and I felt some confidence come back to me.*

*I wish I could say my second at-bat ended with a bomb off the light tower that shattered the bulbs and that, as I rounded the bases, I felt like Roy Hobbs and that familiar tune filled the stadium. Not this time. I struck out. However, I saw the ball clearly and, unlike before, I walked away feeling like I had a chance. My next two at-bats were much better. I hit a double off the wall in right and a single up the middle. I couldn't help but be sad and excited as thoughts like,* I've wasted the last 12 years *and* Wow, I can see the ball so much better, *went back and forth in my head. I'm focused on the possibility that I'm going to be a better hitter for the rest of my career. Hopefully, I will and I'll get an opportunity to get back to the majors. Wish me luck, and don't forget to get your eyes checked.*

Chris was having a great career but still wanted to make it to the "show" (playing for a major league team). He could see better than average, but I was able to make him even better by using lenses to improve his eyesight. There are three ways that eye doctors can make this correction, and Chris used all three. He wore glasses at first. I fit him with a contact lens later. He played with glasses or lenses for a while and then had laser surgery to correct his vision. I have since found that a contact lens over his laser surgery gives him 20/13 vision.

What are eye doctors actually correcting to make athletes see better? Not every eyeball is the perfect shape to form perfect vision. Some eyeballs are longer than average, some are shorter than average, and some have a football shape. These physical differences result in conditions called *nearsightedness* (myopia), *farsightedness* (hyperopia), and *astigmatism*. People with these types of problems can have their vision corrected all the way up to 20/8 if it's genetically possible for their particular eyes. My eyes could only be corrected to my genetic potential of 20/20. I took Chris's eyes up to his 20/13. Everyone's genetic potential is different. That's why athletes with mere mortal eyes like mine should see the eye doctor often to ensure their vision stays as clear as possible, so that they can develop their games to their fullest genetic potential.

Some eye doctors test for *dynamic visual acuity*. This testing method determines how well athletes can distinguish letters on a rotating board. Since an athlete's world is in motion, the thinking is that this measurement can be used to determine who sees better under moving conditions. I don't include this type of test in the ranking method found in Chapter 13, but I believe it could be added as a test to help compare younger athletes to one another.

**Nearsightedness (Myopia)**

This is the most common type of blurred vision in the age group of the elite athletes we're discussing. Nearsighted people can see things clearly close up, but objects far away are blurry. They are "sighted at near." This usually occurs because the eyeball is longer than it should be. The eyeball is like a camera in which light travels through the lens and focuses on the film (or chip, these days). The eyeball also has a lens at the front that focuses images before they hit the retina, which is responsible for sending the images to the brain, at the back. In a nearsighted person, the image goes through the lens, is in focus at a point in front of the retina, but then goes out of focus by the time it hits the retina. When the image hits the retina, the player reacts. Uncorrected nearsighted athletes tend to be slower on their reaction times. Another way to state this is that because the nearsighted eye is longer, the image takes longer to hit the back of the eye, and so the athlete hesitates for a millisecond until the image hits the retina.

As I stated earlier in this book, over the last 30 years the United States has become 66 percent more nearsighted. Right now this is being blamed on the increased use of digital screens, but there are actually a few studies being run to determine exactly why this shift has occurred.

**Farsightedness (Hyperopia)**

Farsighted people can see things far away, but objects viewed up close are blurry, and these people have to work twice as hard as other people to focus on an up-close object. These athletes pass the distance eye tests at screenings or in doctors' offices, causing them to assume they have good vision, when in reality they don't like to read because they have to work their eyes too hard to focus up close. In a farsighted person, the eyeball is usually shorter than it should be. The image comes through the lens, hits the retina blurry, and actually is in focus at a spot behind the retina. Farsighted people are constantly focusing, so doing up-close work or reading small print can give them a headache or cause them to rub their eyes. In sports, their tendencies are to overreact or to react early to everything. Another way to state this is that since the eyeball is short, the image hits the retina before it is focused so the athlete reacts too early.

**Astigmatism**

Astigmatism simply means that the eyeball is not round but is shaped more like a football. The front part of the eye, the cornea, is cone-shaped. This causes the image to be blurry when it hits the retina. People with astigmatism also see better in bright light as opposed to darker situations.

This brings us to the question, "If there is a visual weakness, can an athlete strengthen it?" We can lift weights to become stronger. We can practice batting to improve our reaction time. We can run and swim to become faster. Can we actually take weak areas of vision and fix them? The answer here is a resounding "yes" as well.

The first area of vision that can be fixed in an athlete is visual acuity. It's as easy as going to the eye doctor and making sure that your athlete is seeing as clearly as possible. To succeed in athletic performance, athletes need to use their best correct acuity when playing.

Years ago, I started working with a serious basketball player. She'd been in the sport since she was 10 years old in various AAU teams and on her middle school and high school teams.

She'd always been one of the best athletes of her age and had a pretty accurate shot. Her vision tested 20/20 in the right eye and 20/30 in the left. Even though she knew her left eye was a little blurrier, she felt like her vision was great for her sport and didn't really want to wear prescription glasses.

I told her I knew she was doing well but that visually, I could help make her better. The tendency for basketball players is to miss their shots to the side of the better-seeing eye. She thought back on her free-throw shooting and realized that when she missed, it was usually to the right side. Reluctantly, she tried a contact lens in her left eye. During a routine checkup a few months later, she let me know that she had indeed become a lot more accurate with her shooting and that her confidence was even greater at the free-throw line. She received a scholarship to play college basketball and won't play at all without her contact lens.

> **See to Play Tip 2:**
> *Athletes miss to the side of the better-seeing eye.*

Playing with less than their best corrected acuity may not be the only reason that players don't reach their full potential, but it can be the beginning. This is the first place to look when an athlete is missing in a consistent pattern. Here are a couple more examples to make my point for this tip:

- A high school golfer was consistently missing his putts on the green to the right of the hole. His left eye was one unit off. I fixed him up. He became the Amateur of the Year and earned a scholarship to an NCAA Division I school.
- A professional pool player started missing consistently to

one side, and it was the same story as the golfer. One change in his prescription in one eye, and he did better.

• An avid hunter who started having trouble missing his target to the right had the same story.

Watch your child or young athlete; these tendencies can be seen everywhere. My youngest daughter had been in my office and had her eyes checked a zillion times (along with the eyes of any stuffed animal that she had in her arms at the time). When she was in sixth grade, we went out for a family putt-putt game. I began to realize she was missing her putts to the right. Sure enough, at her next eye exam in my office, I discovered that her left eye was beginning to get nearsighted and she needed her first pair of glasses.

Every athlete wants to be better. Every competitor wants to get the edge. All parents want to give their children that extra bit that will help them achieve to the highest level. Athletic trainers want to help their athletes get the most out of their bodies by improving muscle movement and strength. Coaches want to make sure that they aren't missing that "something" about their athletes that could make them perform at the maximum level. Getting an athlete's eyes checked at an early age and then rechecked at least every year is the first step to ensure that vision isn't getting in the way of reaching peak performance.

At what age should you have your young athlete's eyes evaluated by an eye doctor? I recommend the first eye exam at around the age of two. This is because our visual system really starts to begin its fine-tuning between the ages of two to six years old. If one eye is considerably different than the other, the child's brain may decide to ignore it, causing what's known as a lazy eye or *amblyopia*. After the athlete reaches the age of six or so, the affected eye cannot be corrected to vision better than 20/40. Catching and treating this condition early is essential for developing proper depth perception and visual development. Optometrists use patch therapy to cover the strong eye, forcing the brain to use the weak eye.

We live in a 3-D world. Our two eyes are separated by an average of six centimeters (around two and a half inches). This means that the eyes have two different perspectives in space on the world that we are viewing. The brain consolidates both images to give us *depth perception*. Some athletes have better depth perception than others. I assess depth perception using tests such as stereopsis and contrast sensitivity and use the results to add another score to my ranking system of how well athletes see.

Athletes who are *monocular* or amblyopic are viewing the world mainly from one eye. They still get cues on depth and distance but use other aspects of what is being viewed to determine how far away objects are from them. Amblyopic athletes can still have adequate peripheral vision in the weaker eye. But just like a boxer fights better with two hands instead of one, athletes who have two properly functioning eyes do better than athletes with only one strong eye.

The next step is to find the right eye doctor. As I described earlier, I became interested in optometry and chose it as my profession because it deals with correcting vision, helping the visual system develop, and exploring vision exercises that can improve all aspects of vision. I recommend finding a sports-vision specialist or an optometrist with a background and interest in sports in your area, if at all possible.

Once you've found the right doctor, he or she will make sure you have the exact correction—if one is needed—to give you your best visual acuity. The correction needs to be exact for developing athletes. One unit too weak or too strong can interfere with an athlete's performance and even get in the way of developing eye-hand-body coordination (We'll discuss this a little later in Chapter 6.) Let me give you some examples from athletes who I helped with just a minor prescription change.

One year I evaluated a catcher who played for the Durham Bulls. He had never had to wear glasses. He saw 20/10 without any prescription and passed every vision test and screening he had ever taken. He never went to the eye doctor's office because he had better-than-average vision when tested during his physical exam, and no one felt he needed a more complete exam. I happened to be in the locker room checking some of the other players' eyes, and he decided to let me check him. I found out that he was one unit farsighted (+0.25 D).

After talking with him about how this could affect his game, it turned out he didn't feel he was hitting as well as he could. He seemed to be consistently pulling the ball. His bat was moving too fast. He couldn't figure out how to slow down his bat speed. He reacted too quickly to most pitches. I fit him with a contact lens for that mild prescription, and he began to hit the ball a lot more accurately. This minor prescription actually helped him slow down his bat speed, and he quit pulling the ball as much. His superhuman vision remained the same, but the way his visual system reacted with his hands and body became more fine-tuned. His batting average that year ended up near .400. (Needless to say, I was in high demand from the rest of the players that year!) He became a hitting coach after he finished his playing career.

Another year, I helped an athlete who was on the AAA team for the New York Mets. His team was in town to play against the Durham Bulls. It was shortly after the season had begun, and he wasn't hitting like he knew he could. He arranged to come over to the Bulls' locker room, where I tested his vision. He was wearing contact lenses that were allowing him to see 20/15. I found that his prescription had changed by one unit (-0.25 D) in one eye. I gave him the new prescription, and he noticed his vision was considerably clearer. He also started hitting the ball better and ended up earning the hitting title for the AAA International League. He was named to the league's All-Star team that year as well.

One young man I worked with was a pitcher in the mid-'90s with the Greenville Braves (AA Atlanta Braves). He had a little trouble placing the ball and seeing the catcher's signals in poorly lit stadiums. One unit of change, and three months later he was pitching in the World Series and now wears a championship ring.

An outfielder for the Carolina Mudcats (single-A Pittsburgh Pirates at the time) needed one unit of change in one eye. He ended up having a team hitting-streak record that was unmatched for many years.

> ### See to Play Tip 3:
> ### *Being one unit off in an eye prescription*
> ### *alters an athlete's reaction time.*

If the image is clear before it hits the retina, the body gets in motion too early. If the image is clear after it hits the retina, the body gets in motion too late. If a blurry image hits the retina and is always blurry, the body has to find ways to compensate to complete the reaction. For these reasons, athletes need clear vision at the proper time to begin the body's athletic processes. Acuity is the most basic building block of eye-hand-body coordination, the most basic building block for athletes' timing. Without the proper correction when needed to give the best acuity, the athlete is going to jump the gun, be too late, or just miss reaching his genetic potential.

You've probably lived this story: It's your favorite football team. It's the big game. It's been a tough battle. The score is tight. The clock is winding down. Your team has the ball for what might be their last drive, and they've got a long way to go. The teams walk up to the line and get set. The ball is snapped. The quarterback fakes a handoff and drops back to pass. The offensive linemen are slugging it out with the defensive linemen. The receivers are sprinting as fast as possible and going deep. The quarterback checks off one receiver and then the next. All of a sudden, the quarterback heaves the ball into the air. What a beautiful spiral, a perfect long arc that is headed straight to the receiver near the end zone! The receiver has the defensive back beat by a step. Both men jump to reach the ball. The ball touches the receiver's hands. *It's there! It's there! It's right there!* And somehow, out of nowhere, the ball is bobbled. His eyes were on the ball. The ball was right where it should have been, but the receiver's hands just didn't get completely around it. The ball, the receiver, the defensive back, and your hopes all drop to the ground because the receiver was failed by vision that could have been improved.

## Examples

To illustrate how an uncorrected problem with visual acuity can affect an athlete's performance, consider that:

| An uncorrected nearsighted athlete: | An uncorrected farsighted athlete: |
|---|---|
| Fouls out more to the first-base side batting right-handed | Fouls out more to the third-base side batting right-handed |
| Fouls out more to the third-base side batting left-handed | Fouls out more to the first-base side batting left-handed |
| Throws a baseball short | Throws a baseball long |
| Is short on shots in basketball (air ball!) | Is long on shots in basketball (throws up bricks) |
| Has the football hit his hands before he grasps it | Grabs at the football before it hits his hands |
| Jumps late to an overthrown pass | Jumps too early to catch the football |
| Throws the football slightly behind the receiver | Throws the football too far in front of the receiver |

| An uncorrected nearsighted athlete: | An uncorrected farsighted athlete: |
| --- | --- |
| May not wrap around on a tackle quickly enough | Jumps on a tackle too quickly |
| Is late with a pass in hockey, hitting the other player's foot instead of his stick | Is early with a hockey pass, putting the puck in front of the stick |
| Hits tennis shots short and off more to the same side that generated the hit | Hits tennis shots long and off more to the opposite side from the hit (pulls) |
| Makes soccer passes late and behind the other player | Makes soccer passes early and ahead of the other player |
| Misses shots to the side of the foot that is kicking the soccer ball | Misses shots high and to the opposite side of the foot that's kicking the soccer ball |
| Makes lacrosse passes late and behind the other player | Makes lacrosse passes early and in front of the other player |
| Pushes putts in golf and comes up short | Pulls putts in golf and goes too long |

Let me throw a little curveball at you. If you have an athlete who is farsighted and wearing a prescription that is too strong, he or she will have the tendencies of the nearsighted person above. This is why it is a *must* that an elite athlete be given the *exact* prescription they need. One unit off either way, too strong or too weak, can adversely affect performance. I have found this to be the cause of many athletes falling just short of their full potential.

Once an athlete has gone to the eye doctor, this process must be repeated every year and sometimes even more frequently if the athlete is going through a growth spurt. Young athletes' bodies, including the eyes, are constantly under change. They get taller. Their arms get longer. The actual length of the eyeball, from the front to the back, can continue to change up until they reach their mid-to-late twenties. This can cause changes to the prescription that an athlete needs up to several times in a single year. For people who are serious about their sports, they are at a disadvantage if they do not keep a constant watch on their vision.

Charles Rozanski, the head trainer for the North Carolina State University Wolfpack, provided an example from experience. He was the moderator of a medical panel that I was on during a conference held for coaches, trainers, parents, and athletes. He told the audience about how this type of rapid prescription change happened to a player on the Wolfpack baseball team. The player's vision was corrected with contact lenses during the preseason physicals. Just a few months later, the player came up to him complaining that things seemed a little blurry. Charlie said that that seemed odd because they knew he was seeing well a short time earlier but, sure enough, the player's vision had changed in that short amount of time.

Just as it's important for athletes to have good sports equipment, it's equally important for athletes to have the best eye equipment. Contact lenses are the best option for most athletes to correct their vision, because they give more side vision and aren't affected by sweat and dirt as much as glasses are. For younger athletes who may have a harder time putting contacts in and taking them out, sports eyeglasses can be the best option.

## Sports Eyeglasses

Athletes use different footwear on their feet when they play than they wear when they go to school or when they dress up. It is very important to look at eyeglasses in the same way. The glasses that athletes wear to school usually aren't as durable and safe as the glasses that are made specifically for sports. A pair of regular eyeglasses is a dangerous target for a ball. The frame can break when hit the wrong way and cause a serious injury to the face or eyes. A shattered lens can blind an eye. Sports eyeglasses, on the other hand, are specifically designed to protect the eyes.

There are a lot of options with protective sports eyewear these days, and athletes can even use them to make a cool or intimidating statement. The lenses used are shatterproof. Nonglare lenses are available to filter out glare and help athletes see better in lower-light situations. Yellow or amber tints can be added to improve depth perception. Some glasses are even designed to cut down on fogging. They have come a long way from the one pair of black glasses that was the only choice available when I wore sports glasses.

**Contact Lenses**

This is the most popular option for correcting vision so that athletes can see to play. I also consider contact lenses to be the best option because they provide more peripheral vision than glasses do and can protect the cornea from a fingernail or other object that flies into the eye; the lens acts as a protective layer and takes the brunt of the force.

There are several factors to consider when choosing the right contacts for your athlete.

- Frequency of Replacement: Contacts are available that you can replace every day, every two weeks, or even once a month. In sports that cause more sweat or are played in a dirty environment, contacts should be replaced more frequently. The optical quality of the lenses is usually a little better, however, in the lenses that are designed to last a month. The doctor and athlete need to weigh the benefits versus shortcomings of each option.

- Lens Material: Some lenses are designed to give the eyes more oxygen or allow them to breathe better. Other lenses are designed not to dry out as much. I mostly use soft contact lenses with athletes. Gas-permeable or hard lenses are not used much in sports because they can get knocked out of the eye more easily. For athletes who may need the vision and fitting benefits of gas-permeable lenses, I recommend segmented lenses, which are hard in the middle and soft on the outside. This usually ensures a lens won't get dislodged in play.

- Size: Contacts come in different sizes. A loose-fitting lens will move around too much and may pop out. A tight-fitting lens will actually make the eye start blurring after every blink. Contacts have to fit properly to avoid those situations.

- Proper Use: Sleeping in contacts is a no-no for athletes and should be discouraged. When you sleep in contacts, the cornea swells more than it should during the night. This can decrease depth perception and eventually decrease acuity. This means sleeping in a contact lens can take a 20/10 athlete to 20/20, which is not acceptable. (Note that corneal-reshaping contacts, or orthokeratology, should not be used on athletes. This is a type of therapy that involves wearing specially designed contacts at night to change the shape of the cornea and improve vision. The problem is that during the day or the time spent out of the contact lens, the cornea can shift, and vision may not be as exact as needed for the athlete at performance time.)

- Dry Eyes: Human tears are made of three layers: oil, water, and mucus. All three layers need to function well for the contacts and cornea to remain hydrated. A decrease in the oil layer or increased watering of the eyes throws off this balance and causes the cornea to dry out. This causes uncomfortable eyes and blurred vision. Different types of contact-lens materials can be used to keep dryness to a minimum.

• Astigmatism: People who have astigmatism are harder to fit with contact lenses. Usually, they end up wearing lenses that have a weight at the bottom to keep them in position so that they remain stable in the eye. These lenses are known as *toric* contact lenses. The lens may spin a little and move out of position when the athlete blinks, and the weight brings it back in place. (There's actually more science behind these contacts than the weights, but most people find this weight property the easiest to understand.) If the blinking and consequent spinning mean that the athlete's vision is constantly going from clear to blurry, he or she may need to try more lenses to find one that fits with more stability. Toric lenses can become so annoying that some players find themselves not blinking as much in order to keep the lenses more stable.

MLB player and home-run slugger Mark McGwire is a well-known athlete who succeeded in his sport while wearing contact lenses designed to correct astigmatism. He, like everyone else, would experience the occasional blur from his toric lenses rotating out of position. In order to combat this while he was at bat, he developed a system where he would blink first and let the lenses get into the proper position to make his vision 20/10, then step into the batter's box. He would not blink again until after the pitch came. This routine would ensure that his vision wouldn't fuzz from any shifting of the toric lens so that he could see to hit the ball. He also wore contacts with a slight yellowish tint to help improve his depth perception and block out the haze that blue light causes.

I taught Mark's blink technique to a patient of mine who also was a professional baseball player. He had so much astigmatism that even the smallest rotation of his toric lens would blur his vision. He was fit correctly and with the best lens made for his prescription, but just a slight movement of the lens to the left or right deteriorated his vision. He learned to stand outside the batter's box while he blinked and let the lens get to the correct position so that his vision was clear. He would stop blinking, get into the batter's box, and watch the pitch all the way in. If he had to blink or his vision shifted, he would simply step out for a minute to let them settle and start the routine over.

There is a condition with astigmatism known as *keratoconus*. This is a type of astigmatism that keeps growing. The football shape of the cornea just keeps moving further and further out. This is a genetic trait. I tell people that it's like the story of Pinocchio's nose that kept growing. For athletes with this condition, I have to use contact lenses constructed from harder materials to keep the cornea from moving forward. Keeping in place a cornea that wants to grow further out can be tricky. Fitting a keratoconic patient with a contact lens becomes a balance of slowing the keratoconus from bulging forward and keeping the eye healthy and happy. As I mentioned above, for athletes I use a segmented lens that is hard in the middle and soft on the outer ring so that it won't fall out during play.

Another problem that can happen to athletes who have astigmatism occurs when the lighting is dimmer, such as during games played at night in outdoor settings. The *pupil* (the black center in the iris, or colored part of the eye) gets larger in dim light, and as a result it allows more of the distorting light that is hitting the athlete's football-shaped cornea to get through to the back of the eye. So athletes with astigmatism have more difficulty seeing clearly at night and usually notice a glare coming from the lights.

Here are some general examples of how astigmatism can affect an athlete's performance if not fully corrected:

- Baseball pitchers can't pick up signals from the catcher in night games. Catchers have been known to paint their nails with white correction fluid to help these pitchers out.
- Baseball hitters have trouble picking up the ball from the pitcher's hand in night games.
- Basketball shooters have problems seeing a clear spot on the rim, especially in gyms with low lighting.
- Tennis players have trouble picking up the ball when they toss it in the air for the serve at night.
- Football receivers have trouble picking up the deep ball during night games.
- Golfers tend to shy away from dark sunglasses because it tends to mimic nighttime.

> **See to Play Tip 4:**
> **Astigmatism likes the light and not the dark.**

Chris Richard brought this up when he compared the lights of the Durham Bulls' stadium to the lights of the Richmond stadium. The athlete whose vision remains the most stable when the environmental lighting changes from lighter to darker will more than likely perform better than the athlete who struggles when the lighting changes.

Since I'm talking about lighting, this is a good time to bring up an interview I read with Ted Williams, who is considered to be professional baseball's best hitter of all time. He had super-human vision and reportedly used lighting to his advantage by stepping out of the batter's box if a cloud came over the sun. (This slight darkening causes the pupil to get larger, which can allow more blur to get to the back of the eye.) He said he would back out of the box, act like he was cleaning an imaginary cinder out of his eye, and then either wait for the cloud to leave or let his pupil adjust its dilation. I'm sure he didn't understand why he was doing it, but he had figured out a system that gave him a better feel for the pitch in changing light conditions.

I give a similar suggestion to hitters who have trouble in darker stadiums. I recommend trying to stay under the lights or to look around—but not directly at—the bright stadium lights before getting ready to hit or look at a pitch. This exposure to the light causes the pupils of the eyes to become smaller, which blocks out some of the aberrant light rays that cause glare. This technique takes practice. If you look directly into a light, you'll end up seeing an afterimage, and that will get in the way. The goal is to keep the pupil small but without a distracting afterimage.

Recently, Josh Hamilton and several other blue-eyed base-ball players have brought up another concern about lighting conditions for athletes. These athletes find that their batting averages for day games are not as good as their averages for night games and believe that one reason is because their blue eyes do not absorb light as well as brown eyes do. This difference in eye color causes them to be bothered more by glare on sunny days, which makes it harder for them to see the ball. Many of these athletes have started wearing sunglasses to help improve their vision during bright light and glare situations.

**LASIK and Refractive Surgery**

Tiger Woods is probably the highest-profile athlete who has benefited from LASIK surgery. You may have even seen the commercials where he touts the benefits that he received from the surgery. Reports claim that he went from -11 D to not needing any prescription at all. He had the surgery and a few years later went back to have it touched up, which is known as an "enhancement."

I have been fortunate to work with several great refractive surgeons, and I have even recommended LASIK to professional athletes. I do have a general rule that I tell athletes who are contemplating refractive surgery: if the ball or target in your sport or position is moving away from you, refractive surgery may be a good option; but if the ball or target is coming toward you (especially smaller objects or ones traveling at faster speeds), you may want to wait until you're finished with your sports career.

I recommend refractive surgery for those athletes who:

- Can't be corrected fully with contact lenses, or their contacts move too much and clear vision isn't stable.
- Can't tolerate contact-lens materials or the feeling of having something in their eyes.

The reasons I hesitate to refer athletes for refractive surgery are:

- The results are usually not as exact as with glasses or contacts. The athlete may still end up needing a prescription if he or she is still a unit or two off after the procedure.
- It can increase an athlete's problem with glare.
- It can cause the eyes to dry out more, and the athlete may

have to use moisture drops frequently.

- There's been a rare case or two where an athlete's best corrected acuity was actually worse after the surgery than before, and the use of glasses or contacts could not improve vision back to presurgery levels.

A much-publicized example of someone who dealt with several of these issues at once is Atlanta Braves catcher Brian McCann. He had LASIK surgery before the 2008 season. I haven't read any reports that he had trouble with his eyes during that season. However, at the beginning of the 2009 season, the vision in his left eye became blurry. That eye also became dry and watery. He tried a contact lens for the blurriness and ointments for the dryness. He even had to try glasses with a corrective lens just for his left eye. He had to be put on the disabled list for a while until the situation could be resolved.

Pete Friesen mentioned in Chapter 1 of this book that vision is one of the most underrated attributes of an athlete. I agree with him and would go a step further by saying it's often the most overlooked of an athlete's physical traits. I stated earlier that visual acuity is the most basic building block in an athlete's success, but I think there are several reasons why athletes have the tendency to overlook how they see to play.

- "If it ain't broke, don't fix it." Chris Richard mentioned that he always felt he saw well, so he didn't do anything about his vision. People don't know how well they can see until they visit an eye doctor's office.
- If an athlete has their vision tested at a physician's office, they figure that this type of testing is adequate. As we've discussed, an athlete's vision should be under the highest

scrutiny, like fine-tuning a race car's engine.

- Some athletes are just squeamish about their eyes. We all have a fight-or-flight mechanism that is in our psyche and protects us from harm. Some athletes freak out when another human being, like an eye doctor, gets that close to their eyes. I've even had some athletes get faint when they are being tested.

- Athletes don't like knowing there is a chink in their armor. Seeing is so basic that if they find out that they are less than superhuman, this is deemed a weakness. No athlete wants to have a weakness.

- There is an unfortunate negative stigma out there about wearing glasses. I was called "Four Eyes" as a young athlete. Chris said he felt that getting called "Specs" would be worth it since he could see so much better.

- Athletes who went to the eye doctor and got a great checkup or who were once prescribed a correction get the feeling they never have to return; they assume vision doesn't change. As I stated, the eyes are like other parts of the body that continue to grow and change. Athletes need to continually have their vision tested.

Again, whatever reason people use for staying away, athletes need to change their mind-set and get evaluated at the eye doctor's office at least once a year. Athletes will go to any length to make their bodies and muscles stronger. They'll spend big bucks on equipment that promises to make them perform better in their sport. They'll take whatever supplements are needed to help the body perform at its peak level. (Some may even go as far as to use banned substances to increase their strength.) But they won't go find out if their visual system can be tweaked to improve vision and eye-hand-body coordination. Sounds crazy, I know.

I hope this chapter has helped you realize how important it is to get your athlete's eyes evaluated at a young age and then rechecked often. The slightest deficiency in visual acuity can get in the way of how the body responds to what the athlete sees. Athletes must have the clearest vision possible so that they can see to play to their genetic potential.

# CHAPTER 3
## SEE WIDE FOR CHAMPIONSHIP SIDE VISION

Peripheral vision always comes up when people talk about the traits that help make athletes great. Walter Payton not only saw the play unfold and small holes open up on the football field but could see second- and third-level defenders. Sportscasters break down for us how Tom Brady and Peyton Manning can walk up to the line of scrimmage, read a defense, get the ball from the center, drop into the pocket, know where the receivers and defenders will be, and still have the awareness to sense when the pocket is caving. Michael Jordan can be found on video teaching players not to look at the ball or the opposing players, but to fixate on a spot between them so that both can be seen in the same gaze. Sportswriters rave about the court vision of LeBron James and argue over whether his is better than that of Larry Bird. Wayne Gretzky stated that because of his smaller size, he learned to be aware of everything going on off to his sides during a hockey game.

The vision that I am talking about here is known as peripheral or side vision. Visual acuity deals with the image that an athlete has in his or her straight-ahead gaze, like the *E* on the vision chart. Side vision encompasses the rest of the images on the chart as well as the wall the chart is on, the floor and ceiling attached to that wall, the person standing beside the chart giving the test, the tables and chairs in the room, the athlete's nose and other visible body parts—basically everything else in the room that is visible to the athlete other than the letter *E*. Side vision encompasses a much larger area of space in the athlete's total vision, even though the objects in that space are less clear and distinct than the target of the athlete's visual acuity.

Athletes rely on the information from their side vision and process it differently than visual acuity. The brain uses two visual streams to process visual information. The *ventral visual stream* is used for object recognition, such as reading the letter on a chart. The *dorsal visual stream* uses our side vision more and helps athletes know where they are in space and time. The dorsal visual stream feeds information to the brain along with input from other body systems to help keep athletes in proper orientation to the things around them as well as allowing them to project where other objects will be in space and time. The dorsal and ventral visual streams work together but are also split apart so that the brain can be more efficient in getting the body going. They also work to get the right side of the brain to talk to the left side.

A recent study of inexperienced versus expert chess players is a good illustration of how this works. Both groups were found to recognize individual chess pieces at the same speed. However, when shown chess patterns, the inexperienced players looked at the individual pieces while the expert players looked in the middle of the pattern and used their peripheral vision to take in the information quicker. This allowed the expert chess players to solve the problems faster. Brain scans of the study partici-pants lit up with increased activity in the areas of the brain that were being used the most. It turns out that the expert players were actually using more of their brains to process the available information.

Can you just imagine doing brain scans on Tom Brady and

Peyton Manning to find out how their brains light up when they read a defense before the play starts? Imagine how Michael Jordan's brain scan would have looked as he was coming down the lane reading a defense and getting ready to make the spectacular Air Jordan move. You'd probably have to put sunglasses on to read the brain scans of these athletes because of how intense and bright their brains light up!

I believe side vision is one of the most important components of the visual system when it comes to working with athletes. Visual acuity is the hero when it comes to comparing athletes to each other and predicting which athletes may turn elite. This makes side vision the unsung hero. Elite athletes have great visual acuity, as I discussed in Chapter 2, but they also have great side vision. Not only that, their areas of visual acuity seem to encompass a larger zone, allowing them to see things in a clearer fashion by simply placing their gaze in the middle of the action and paying attention to the things going on around them.

I have the privilege of working with Hockey Hall of Fame member Ron Francis. He credits his keen side vision as being one of the traits that helped him become the second all-time regular-season assist leader in the NHL behind Wayne Gretzky. Ronnie played for the Hartford Whalers; went to the Pittsburgh Penguins, where he won two Stanley Cups; and then finished his career with the Carolina Hurricanes. He could see a bigger picture of where everyone was on the ice, which helped him pass the puck to the right spot so that a teammate could take the shot to score. He told me that he would often check his side vision with his fingers and use other techniques to keep it tuned up. Working with elite players like him has helped me develop my philosophy on testing and training side vision, and you'll find exercises that can help you and your athletes develop better side vision later in the book.

I have also had the privilege of providing eye care for Pro Bowl and NFL Super Bowl champion Torry Holt. He has been in the NFL since 1999 and won Super Bowl XXXIV with the St. Louis Rams. I asked him if there was anything that I could share with you about his vision that helped him become an elite athlete. He told me that, hands down, it is his ability to see everything on the football field as a play occurs and unfolds as he anticipated, using both his wide field of view and intense mental preparation using visualization (which I discuss in Chapter 8).

When Torry hears a play called, he visualizes what the goal of the coach is by choosing that play. As he approaches the line of scrimmage, he sees where his opponents are, in front of him and also to either side. He senses each of their roles in the play. He uses his detailed vision zone to visually incorporate the next level of defenders—who are beyond the line of scrimmage—determines where they are looking, and visualizes where they are headed. He adds the third level of defense to his field of view. Finally, he uses all of this information to get to the right place to make the play a success.

Throughout his NFL career, this ability has caused many of his peers to ask him the same question: "How did you see that?"

While side-vision traits are often talked about when describing great athletes, no one ever seems to talk about an actual physical measurement. I break down side vision into two different zones and measure the size of each zone. I rank athletes with larger zones of vision higher than those with smaller zones.

In the last chapter, I stated that visual acuity is the basic building block for predicting which athletes will become elite.

With acuity as the building block, peripheral vision is the mortar that holds the building blocks together to create a strong foundation. And the more mortar you have, the more building blocks you can put together. Athletes with a larger area of peripheral vision have a bigger view of the playing field. Because of this, I place equal emphasis on side vision and visual acuity in my overall ranking method. I refer to the two types of side vision that I test and rank as:

• Detailed vision zone
• Extreme side vision

**Detailed Vision Zone**

I'll talk about this zone first because this is where elite athletes excel over the average athlete by the biggest margin. Most eye doctors refer to this general area by the term *central peripheral awareness*. I put a more specific name on the zone of vision that I am referring to because I take measurements to define its size. This zone represents how far detailed vision goes into the periphery before it becomes a generalized blur.

The easiest way to learn about this zone is by testing yourself. I need you to grab a deck of playing cards and find an ace in the deck, then hold it in your right hand with the *A* facing you. Now sit in a chair about 10 feet away from something that is at the same level as your eyes, such as a light switch. Fix your gaze on the very tip of the light switch. Throughout this exercise, it is important that you do not allow yourself to look off to the right or the left of the switch.

We're going to test your right eye first, so close or patch your left eye. Extend your right arm completely out with the *A* facing you and move it to an area that puts it at about a 45-degree angle to the right of the light switch. You should be able to see the light switch, your arm, and your card to the right, but you should not be able to distinguish the letter *A*. Slowly bring the card toward the light switch and stop when you can first make out that the letter is an *A*. This represents the right outside or temporal limit of the detailed vision zone in your right eye.

Transfer the card to your left hand, and extend your arm in the same fashion so that the card that is facing you now is at a 45-degree angle to the left of the light switch. Leave your left eye closed or patched. Again, slowly bring the card toward the light switch and stop when you can first distinguish the letter *A*. This represents the right inside or nasal limit of your right eye's detailed vision zone.

The average athlete can distinguish the letter *A* out to about 15 degrees to the right of the light switch and about the same 15 degrees or so to the left of the switch. The size of the detailed vision zone is calculated by adding the two numbers together, which in this case is a total of 30 degrees. Elite athletes begin to show their visual superiority by being able to still see the letter *A* as they move it out past the 25-degree mark to an area between 30 to 40 degrees to the right side or left side of the switch. This means they have a potential for their detailed vision zone to extend up to 80 degrees!

---

***See to Play Tip 5:***
***Elite athletes have a larger detailed vision zone.***

---

You'll notice I didn't mention the measurement of the vertical aspect of the detailed vision zone. I haven't gotten involved with measuring this dimension of the zone much because my current focus is working with a professional hockey team. I'm trying to compare and predict which athletes are going to be the best, using the traits of their visual skills. Hockey uses more horizontal side vision than vertical side vision. If I were performing these evaluations for a professional football team's skilled athletes or for a professional basketball team, I would also evaluate the vertical range of the detailed vision zone and add those results to my ranking system for the athletes, because those sports depend on vision in the vertical zone.

The detailed vision zone is determined physiologically by receptors in our retina known as cones. You may remember that cones give us our acuity, our high-definition vision. They are also responsible for our color vision. Cones are concentrated in the center of the retina, in an area known as the macula or *fovea*. This area consists primarily of cones and is the center of our vision.

I tell people to think of the physical size of the macula, which is responsible for the detailed vision zone, as you would the bull's-eye on a dartboard. This is the area that gives us our best vision. Some people are born with larger bull's-eyes than others. Through measuring the detailed vision zone, I am in a sense finding out how big the bull's-eye is for each athlete. The larger the zone, the better I predict the athletes will perform. The size of this area is a genetic trait determined at birth, but some believe, like I do, that the perception in this area can shrink from lack of use.

The detailed vision zone is an area where I think we can help athletes improve their game. Some athletes have the physical skills of the elite but have a decreased or smaller detailed vision zone. I recommend eye exercises to these athletes to wake up the cones at the edge of the range and try to expand it to its fullest possible level.

Scientifically, we know that there is a physical limit to each athlete's cone area, so our ability to expand this range of vision is limited. But if we can wake up any cones that may have fallen asleep from lack of use or if we can help athletes expand their attention range so that they can reach a higher potential as athletes, then the exercises definitely have worth.

When I measure an athlete's detailed vision zone, I perform a test that is much more exact than the test you just performed on yourself. I use a vision disk, which is a piece of equipment with markings on it, similar to those on a protractor, that allow the tester to measure a number of degrees away from the center spot of focus. The athlete stares at the same central target during the entire test period. Letter cards are moved in from the side in an arc fashion around the eyes until the athlete can read them. The cards are at a distance of 16 inches away from the eyes throughout the test. The letter size used in this test is about the same size as the lettering on a playing card, or about the same as the 26-point font size of the bold Times New Roman found in Microsoft Word. (For those of you who want more information on vision disks and testing cards, please refer to www.seetoplay. com.)

Athletes are very competitive with this testing, so the urge to peek at the card happens often. I change the card to a new one when I catch them looking off to the side. I also use several different letters so that the athletes cannot memorize one or two letters and guess the correct answer. I also motivate them to try to feel their side vision stretching. When I catch them looking over to see the letter, I don't respond to this negatively but instead say, "Great job! That's normal to want to look at the target. Let's start the test."

When I use this testing method, I find that the average athlete has an area of about 10 to 20 degrees on either side of the center spot, adding up to a score in the range of 20 to 40 degrees. Elite athletes' detailed vision zone stretches out past 25 degrees on either side of the center spot and usually falls between 30 and 40 degrees. Their total score starts above 50 degrees and may extend out to 80 degrees.

One year when I showed Pete Friesen how the players ranked visually with their detailed vision zones, he joked that I could've just put them in order of their salaries or by who's mentioned in the newspaper the most. And, in a sense, he was right. The best-performing athletes, the stars, scored and ranked the highest.

I have included exercises later in this book designed to help athletes keep their detailed vision zones tuned up. My favorite exercises include the Detailed Vision Read and also the Scrabble Pieces Read. These are simple exercises that require little space or equipment. They can be done while sitting, or you can add difficulty by moving or working out on a stationary bike. Your goal when working out and performing the eye exercises is to expand the detailed vision zone.

Another easy way to understand and work on your detailed vision zone involves looking at a piece of artwork. Stand about three feet away and try to have your eyes level with the middle of the picture. While you stare at the middle of the picture, try to make out details of the rest of the picture. Slowly move your attention—but not your eyes—outward. Can you make out other things in the picture? Can you tell what color those things are? Try to expand the area of the picture that you can make out. (Professional athletes like to use that exercise when they are on the road. They're spending many nights in different hotel rooms, and those rooms always have a piece of artwork.)

Why is a larger detailed vision zone important for athletes? Let me give you an example using two football players. Player A has been tested to have a detailed vision zone of 30 degrees, and Player B has a zone of 75 degrees. Imagine these two athletes rushing to the line of scrimmage with the football. They are looking for the hole to hit while avoiding the defenders trying to tackle them. Player B is going to see twice as much detail in one area of gaze compared to Player A. Player A will have to move his head and eyes more to get the same field of vision as Player B, meaning he may take his eye off the hole that is getting ready to open to his right in order to find the defender who may hit him on the left. Player B sees all this without moving his head out of position. People talk about running backs who have the ability to see holes open up and visualize the running lanes, and Player B in this example has great ease with his larger detailed vision zone. Not only that, Player B has a larger zone, allowing him to see up the field to avoid the next level of defenders, while Player A will again have to shift his head to gain the same view.

Now imagine how that larger detailed vision zone helps a:

- Basketball player see to make the pass or get a steal
- Baseball player see the field to make the double play
- Hockey player see the ice, teammates, and opponents
- Soccer player see more of the field for teammates and scoring opportunities
- Tennis player see the full court to place shots

I also believe that the detailed vision zone is the essential building block for helping athletes achieve *the zone*. What zone am I talking about here? By "the zone" I mean the athletic state of nirvana where time seems to slow down and everything appears larger, allowing the athlete to achieve at the highest level. Athletes in the zone refer to this state in very similar terms.

They will say things to the effect of:

- "I was really in the zone today."
- "The ball appeared much larger."
- "The players around me were moving in slow motion."
- "Everything was really vivid on the court today."

Sports psychologists will tell you that the zone is a state of mind. It is. I believe that the zone is also based on an area of vision. My thinking is that those athletes who have larger areas of vision seem to report more frequently about playing in the zone. I've talked to all types of athletes. The elite seem to have the edge over the average in achieving the zone, and they also have larger detailed vision zones. Their vision has a bigger canvas for the mind to paint on. They take in more visually. They can process more visual information. They figure things out quicker. (Remember, their brain scans are probably lighting up more.)

I also believe that the ability to reach the zone has an acquired component to it as well, in that you have to practice, practice, practice. Going back to the chess players, the study suggested that the main reason the expert players were better at pattern recognition was because they had so much more practice time, which helped them fine-tune the brain's processing of this visual system. My belief is that if you have a young athlete with a large detailed vision zone and you add a bunch of practice, practice, practice, watch out! There is an elite athlete in the making.

Conversely, it's my belief that athletes with smaller detailed vision zones will probably report having more problems achieving the zone or even understanding it. From interviewing athletes in whom I've measured smaller detailed vision zones, this seems to be the general rule that I've found. This means that if you have a young athlete with a small detailed vision zone, you really need to add more practice time to help this athlete catch up. The vision exercises that you will find in this book are invaluable in helping these athletes overcome a big obstacle that can interfere with their chances of becoming elite.

I'll finish my discussion on the detailed vision zone by talking about the little guy on the field or court who is smaller in physical stature but is still outachieving the opposition. Just like I stated in Chapter 2, these athletes usually have better visual acuity, and I guarantee you they also have a larger detailed vision zone. This type of vision can help the athlete see more than their larger opponents who have smaller vision zones. They take in more information, process it, and move accordingly. An expanded detailed vision zone can be a great equalizer.

**Extreme Side Vision**

*Extreme side vision* is the term that I use to refer to the limit of how far each of us can see out to the right and left of our bodies when we stare at an object straight ahead. You can test this on yourself by sitting in front of the same light switch that you used to determine your detailed vision zone. You are allowed to keep both eyes open this time, and use the same ace from the deck of playing cards that you used before. Extend your right arm straight out to your right side so that it is even with your right ear. This represents about 90 degrees of vision to the right of your fixation spot. If you can see the card, move it back behind you more; you have greater than 90 degrees of extreme side vision to your right side. If you have to move the card in from the 90-degree location, then you have less than 90 degrees. In this measurement, you do not need to see the letter *A*; you just need to see the movement of the card as it enters your field of vision. You can then repeat this with your left hand on your left side and find your left extreme-side-vision range.

I use the same vision disk to measure athletes' extreme side vision as I use to test the detailed vision zone. The athletes must continue to look at the same fixation spot without moving their eyes to the right or left while I bring a card in from behind their heads on both the right and left side. I record the degree marker when an athlete first states that the card has moved into view and add the number that I find on the right to the number on the left to come up with the extreme-side-vision score. The average athletes see the card between 80 and 90 degrees on each side, giving them a measurement of 160 to 180 degrees. Elite athletes measure out 100 to 110 degrees on each side, for a total measurement of 200 to 220 degrees.

---

**See to Play Tip 6:**
*Elite athletes have a larger area of extreme side vision.*

---

The area of extreme side vision is provided by receptors in our retina known as *rods*. They are found surrounding the area of the cones and move all the way out to the periphery of the retina. Using my dartboard analogy, the cones are the bull's-eye and the rods are the rest of the dartboard. Just like some athletes have larger bull's-eyes, some athletes have larger dartboards. Elite athletes have larger areas of extreme side vision, but the gap between elite and average athletes in this area of vision is less than that of the detailed vision zone.

Rods give us information on movement, surroundings, and our body's position in space. The visual acuity of the rods is not very good. That's why we can't read print or distinguish detail—like the faces of people off to the side—but we can tell that something is there. Rods are responsible mainly for detecting motion and for night vision.

An interesting note here is that people who have amblyopia or a lazy eye still use that eye for detecting motion. The brain ignores this weaker eye during normal vision but will turn it on when it detects something moving in from the side. This is a basic survival trait. An example of this would be a driver who has a great left eye and a weak or lazy right eye. If an animal runs out on the road from the right, the driver's brain will turn on the side vision of the right eye, so that the driver can move the left eye into position to see what's moving and then make the correct move to avoid the animal.

So images that are out of the detailed vision zone but are still in our extreme side vision are viewed as objects with movement but without detail. Let's go back to our quarterback talk. The quarterback drops back in the pocket to pass. The detailed vision zone allows the quarterback to read the defense and see the detail of the play that's unfolding. His extreme side vision is what feeds information into his brain about the state of the pocket of protection his linemen are providing for him. Is the pocket caving in? Is there a blitz on and a defender moving in on him? Is there a defender rushing in from the side to try and pick off the pass near the receiver? The quarterback with the larger range of extreme side vision will be able to take in more information visually, while the quarterback with the smaller range will have to move his head more to see the same amount of field.

Athletes describe using this type of vision several ways:

- "I could sense where everyone was on the court today."
- "I had great presence today and could feel when I was getting in trouble."

• "I saw the play from the outside in real well today."

Athletes use their extreme side vision in almost every sport. I used the quarterback example above because it was easy to illustrate. The same could be said of basketball or soccer. Another example of athletes who use a lot of this type of side vision is triathletes. In particular, during the swimming segment, triathletes use peripheral clues around them to let them know where they are on the course and in relation to the other athletes.

I had a discussion with a patient of mine who is a triathlete. I asked him to explain how he used his side vision. He told me that he would scout the course the day before the race. Many of the swims are in lakes, so he would look around to pick out large visual markers so that he could use them to map out in his head how far along he was in the swim. He chose things that wouldn't move, like water towers, boat houses, and docks. He was also careful to select objects that he would be able to see with his side vision during the swim, so that he could tell if he was swimming in a straight line or zigzagging, especially if there was a current in the water. Just to complicate things, other swimmers in the water tend to be close during a race, which can cause a lot of splashing and make vision tasks more difficult. (We'll discuss visual noise in Chapter 7).

Since this visual area deals more with objects and movement than with detail, the best way to train or exercise it is with objects in motion. One of my favorite exercises (included in Chapter 12 later in this book) has the athlete sit in a chair looking straight ahead while a trainer moves different objects, like a baseball, soccer ball, stuffed animal, football, or hat from behind the athlete into his extreme side vision while the athlete guesses the object being shown. There are several others, including the Side

Vision Swing Exercise, in Chapter 12 for you to try.
Exercising this visual area is important because:

• This area is believed to shrink with disuse.
• Athletes report this type of vision shrinks as they fatigue.

You'll find that I recommend doing some of the exercises
while on a stationary bike or while fatigued. Many athletes report
to me that they feel their side vision seems to shrink when they
get exhausted. I'll hear them say things like, "That guy came out
of nowhere," or, "I swear I didn't see him until the last second."
Exercising athletes' peripheral vision while they are also exercising their bodies will help train the brain to continue to use those
receptors far out in the retina.

Some athletes who sustain concussions are affected in the
way that the brain uses the information from the ventral and
dorsal visual streams. Concussions can affect many different
parts of the brain, but when the visual system is involved, it's
usually because these two visual systems don't work together as
well. I'll discuss this in more detail in Chapter 10, but it warrants
mention here as an introduction to the subject.

I'll end this chapter by discussing how the results of my
side-vision tests factor into my ranking method. First off, I rank
each athlete by the size of his detailed vision zone. The second
ranking compares the size of each athlete's extreme side vision.
Combined, these two side-vision rankings are weighted equally
to visual acuity in the overall visual ranking of the athlete.

This warrants repeating because I feel it's so important: I
weigh the ranking of side vision with equal importance to visual
acuity. Both are genetically predetermined traits. Just as you
can't give an athlete better acuity than their genetic potential,

you can't expand peripheral vision zones past what is physiologically present in the eye. What you can do is improve peripheral vision awareness with vision exercises to ensure you're reaching your genetic potential and that your side-vision zones are fully awake and functioning.

Again, Eric Staal and Cam Ward of the Carolina Hurricanes have allowed me to share that they have consistently scored as having the largest detailed vision zones (up to 80 degrees) and extreme side vision (over 200 degrees) when compared to other athletes I've evaluated. Eric plays as a center in hockey. In this position, he has to put the puck through a small opening around the opponent's goalie to score, pass to teammates on all sides who are moving at speeds up to 30 miles an hour, and receive passes from all angles. Cam is a goalie who has to monitor the location of five opposing players who are moving at up to 30 miles an hour in all areas of the ice and also monitor the movement of the puck as it is being passed and then block it from scoring when an opponent takes a shot. These athletes provide excellent examples of players who benefit from having large areas of peripheral awareness.

NFL great Torry Holt has also said that I could share his measurements and, as you would guess, his detailed vision zone is large (up to 80 degrees) as is his extreme side vision (around 200 degrees). It is understandable why he feels that his wide field of view has been a big part of making him so successful as a wide receiver in the NFL. Elite athletes have better vision, and they also have a larger zone of this great vision, which gives them the edge to see to play.

# CHAPTER 4
## MOVE YOUR EYES!

In 2005 when professional golfer Michael Campbell was playing in the US Open Golf Championship at Pinehurst, North
Carolina, people started noticing that he kept running to the
bathroom every five holes or so. They began to wonder if he was
sick or if something was wrong. Turns out, his right eye would
not turn in properly when addressing his golf ball. He was actually running to the bathroom so that he could concentrate on
the eye exercises he used to strengthen his eye muscles. He went
on to win the championship and kiss the trophy. (I just recently
watched him explain this method online in an interview that was
archived on the Golf Channel website. You can find the website
address in my reference section.)

The muscles that move our eyes are similar to other muscles
in our bodies in that they may not be working to their fullest
potential. But we can exercise them to make them work better.

My middle daughter is in the next room working out to the
P90X Extreme Home Fitness series. She has dumbbells in her
hands and is doing bicep curls to work her arms. For those of
you who are not familiar with this program, it is a 90-day home-
fitness program that gets people in great shape. My wife and I
also started the program but had to drop out when our bodies discovered muscles that we had forgotten we had and they
started screaming at us! (In all fairness to the program, we didn't
heed the warning to begin slowly and work at a level where we

felt comfortable. Instead, we tried to keep up with our young whippersnapper daughter!)

In this chapter, I'll describe how our eye muscles work to get the eyes pointing in the right direction to collect information; for athletes, it's information needed to make the desired athletic move. I'll talk about how efficiently the eye muscles of elite athletes work. I'll suggest ways that you can work out your eye muscles and give reasons why you should. The two chapters at the end of this book are dedicated to eye exercises so that you can work out your eye muscles in the same way that my daughter uses her exercise routine to strengthen her body's muscles.

There are two basic aspects of the visual system that I will discuss in this chapter:

1. An athlete's eyes should point directly at the object he or she is viewing and not off to the right or left or in front or behind. An athlete whose eyes are misaligned will miss in the direction that the eyes are pointing.

2. The eye muscles should have the strength to produce an image that is not doubled, even as the eyes work to follow an object that is moving closer or farther away. An athlete whose eye muscles aren't working together as a team will have trouble reaching his or her genetic potential.

**Eye Dominance**

The first step in understanding eye alignment and muscle strength is to determine your *dominancy*—which eye is your dominant eye. So, let me ask you a few questions.

- Which hand do you use to throw a ball?
- Which hand do you use when you write?
- Which eye do you use the most when you line up a shot?

I bet you've never really thought about that last question before!

Just like we prefer to use one hand for throwing and writing, the brain has one eye that it uses more than the other. This is known as our dominant eye.

### Same-Side Dominancy

In general, if you are right-handed, your brain usually uses your right eye more. If you are left-handed, your brain usually prefers the left eye. This is known as *same-side dominancy*. Same-side dominancy is considered to be a plus for sports such as golf. It allows the player to align his or her dominant eye directly over the back of the ball before striking it. A right-handed, right-eyed athlete who is in the best position for the stance and mechanics of a golf swing stands with his right eye directly over the back edge of the ball. If that same person's left eye is the dominant eye, he would have to scoot to the right about two inches in order for his left eye to be directly over the back edge of the ball, which would necessarily affect the mechanics of his swing. Same-side dominancy is generally helpful in sports where the athlete has to aim, such as football, basketball, hockey, soccer, tennis, archery, riflery, pool (billiards), darts, etc.

### Cross-Dominancy

*Cross-dominancy* is when a left-handed person's brain prefers the right eye more or a right-handed person's brain prefers the left eye more. Cross-dominancy is usually considered to be a plus for baseball hitters. Why is that? If you have a right-handed batter in their batting stance, the left eye is the more exposed eye and has a better view of the path of the baseball. As the ball is pitched, the batter's left eye has the better angle to follow it in. You may notice that right-handed hitters who aren't cross-dominant tend to move their chin to the left more to expose the right eye to the pitch a little better.

How do you determine eye dominancy? The easiest way is to extend both arms fully out in front of you, with the index finger and thumb forming an *L* in the left hand and a backward *L* in the right hand. Bring your hands together so that the two *L*s form a diamond shape. Bring one hand slightly in front of the other and continue to make this diamond smaller until the shape is about one inch across. Now, with your arms held about 30 degrees down from your line of gaze, look for an object about 15 feet away, like a picture hanging on a wall. As you continue to fixate on that object, slowly raise your hands up until your fixation point is directly in the middle of the space between your hands. Next, close your left eye while keeping your right eye open. If you still see the object, you're right-eye dominant. If the image is gone, then you are left-eye dominant; you should see the image again when you open your left eye and close your right eye. It is important to make sure you are only seeing the image with one eye. If the fixation hole between the fingers is too big, you will see the image with both eyes and that invalidates the test. If that happens, just bring your hands in closer together so that one eye is eventually blocked.

It is important for athletes and their doctors to ensure the dominant eye is corrected to better visual acuity than the non-dominant eye. If it isn't, athletes will usually miss to the side of the nondominant eye. This really throws off athletes. As a result, they try to adjust all types of mechanics, body position, and movement, which never really works to get them in sync. I've seen athletes struggle needlessly because they failed to make this easy fix.

Archery and riflery (and even golf to some extent) are where
I've seen the most interference from unrecognized cross-dominancy. When I've seen this problem, the athlete uses the dominant eye to line up the shot and then misses to the nondominant
side. Once I can determine that cross-dominancy is a factor for
athletes in these sports, I can recommend eye exercises that help
the athletes suppress or ignore the dominant eye when lining up
the shot, thus resulting in a more favorable outcome. The easiest exercise for correcting this is the Paper Towel Roll exercise,
which you can find in Chapter 12.

Let me give you a real-life example. A hunter came into my
office who was learning to bow hunt. He was having trouble
missing to the right when shooting his bow. I did a few tests
and found out he was right-handed but left-eye dominant. I had
him draw his bow and observed his procedure for lining up a
shot. Sure enough, he was turning his head to the right to get the
right eye out of the way so he could aim with his left eye. This
actually caused him to shoot right of target. I taught him the
Paper Towel Roll exercise to help him be more comfortable aiming with his right, nondominant eye. As he learned to turn on
his right eye in the aiming process, his face became more in line
with his body, which made his shot become more in line as well.
(Another option was to have him learn to shoot the bow from a
left-handed stance, but this was too awkward for him to do.)

> ### See to Play Tip 7:
> ### *Learn which eye you're aiming with and use it wisely.*

I'd like to give another example of an athlete who had a
problem with how she was using her dominant and nondominant eyes. She plays in the LPGA as a right-handed golfer but is

left-eye dominant. She came to my office because she was having trouble getting her game to the level that she wanted. She, like all golfers, consistently works to improve the mechanics of her swing, but she thought she should also check to see if something else was wrong. She'd had several eye exams in the past and wore contact lenses but heard about me and wanted to have a High Performance Vision exam. I diagnosed her with cross-dominancy. We determined that she was placing her nondominant eye over the striking edge of the ball.

We began to discuss her options. Since she was in the middle of the competition year, we decided against moving her back an inch in her stance over the ball to put her dominant eye in the proper position, because this would throw off her swing mechanics. Instead, she used the Paper Towel Roll exercise to strengthen the brain's ability to use information from her nondominant eye. She felt that this helped her finish out the last half of the season considerably stronger than the first half.

In the off-season, we tried to change her stance over the ball to use her dominant eye in hopes of giving her some more consistency, but that ultimately did not work because she felt so comfortable with her original swing mechanics. We ended up going back to our original strategy of strengthening the brain's use of the nondominant eye for aiming purposes through exercises.

You noticed I talked about the "striking edge of the ball" above. For the best aiming accuracy, it is important that the aiming eye be placed directly even with the striking edge of the ball. This helps us hit a ball more accurately. In balls that are thrown, like a free throw in basketball, the aiming eye should be in line with a spot between the first and second knuckle of the throwing hand and the exact point in space that is the visual target.

For those of you who are golfers and haven't learned this trick, I'll describe a method that is designed to show you where your eye is aimed over a golf ball. Place a small, flat mirror on the floor, then put a golf ball in the middle of the mirror. With your putter, address the ball as if you are getting ready to putt it to a certain spot in the room. Look down and focus your aiming eye on the ball as you would if you were getting ready to putt on a green. Draw back the putter head and look below the ball into the mirror to observe where your eye is aligned and pointing. Ideally, the pupil of your eye should be directly over the striking edge of the ball (where the putter first hits) as viewed from your reflection in the mirror. It is surprising to find that the aiming eyes of most average golfers are usually lined up to a spot below the ball (closer to the player's side) and a little further back (away from the hole) than this ideal.

Not all sports require that an athlete look at a specific spot, but it is interesting to note that athletes in many other sports do place their gaze in specific areas. I interviewed Mary Whipple, coxswain for the gold medal-winning women's eight rowing team at the 2008 Beijing Olympic Games and silver medal winner in the 2004 Athens Olympics. She told me that as the "eyes" and driver of the boat (the only one of the crew who is actually watching visually what is occurring in the race), her gaze is usually at a spot beyond the boat. During a race, she moves her gaze to the specific locations of markers and to competitors, scanning as well as using her peripheral vision. The rowers, on the other hand, don't use their eyes actively during competition because they are facing away from where the boat is traveling. These athletes also have specific places that they gaze to help them concentrate on their strokes. This may be the back of the next rower, the oarlock where the oar is attached to the boat, or at a point on the horizon. By deliberately using their eyes in this manner, they can control visual noise to concentrate on their bodies and use their mind's eyes. (We'll discuss both visual noise and the mind's eye in more detail in separate chapters later in this book.)

### Eye Alignment

Now that you know which eye you should be using for your aiming, you need to make sure that it's pointing at the correct spot. Not only that, but your nondominant eye better be pointing to the same spot, or your depth perception will be off. When I talk about eye alignment, I am talking about both eyes pointing in the correct direction. Some athletes' eyes line up exactly, others' do not. I use this information in my vision-ranking system, and the athletes with better alignment are deservedly given a higher ranking.

There are a couple of different ways that your eyes can be pointing in the wrong direction. The first and most common misalignment is having the eyes point off a little to the left or right of the object that you are viewing. When this happens with athletes, they tend to miss in the direction that their eyes are pointing. A second misalignment occurs when the eyes are pointing slightly in front of or slightly behind the object they are viewing. Athletes with this issue tend to miss by being short or long on their aiming. A third type of misalignment is considerably rarer: the eyes can point to a location that is slightly above or below the object that they are viewing. This type of misalignment usually occurs when there has been an injury to the eye such as an orbital blowout fracture.

## Left or Right

There are a couple of simple ways to test if an athlete's eyes are pointing to the left or right of a target. The first is by having the athlete throw darts at the bull's-eye on a dartboard three to five times. The first dart usually is the best predictor of any misalignment, the second dart shows a correction, and the remaining darts tend to walk from the misalignment toward the bull's-eye. Another easy test is to place a piece of tape on a wall at an athlete's eye level and then have that athlete stand 10 feet away and throw a beanbag at the tape using an underhand toss. Just like the results from throwing a dart, you can determine whether the athlete tends to be off to the right or left.

Laser putters are a more sophisticated way to demonstrate if an athlete has the tendency to point the eyes to the right or left. These are putters that have laser beams in them that shine to show where a golfer is pointing. Here, the athlete is supposed to hold the putter with the face pointing toward a target as if to hit a golf ball to roll over it. The laser is turned on so that the athlete can see his or her alignment.

Most golfers have learned to compensate for the fact that they may be off to the left or right. They do this either by pointing their bodies in the other direction, away from the misalignment, or changing how the club face is oriented by opening it or closing it more. An example would be a right-handed golfer whose perception is off to the right. He will either close the club head when putting or open his stance more to the left to compensate for this misalignment. The golfers who improve are the ones who learn to recognize this tendency, compensate for the misalignment of their eyes, and use proper mechanics.

Actually, most athletes have learned to compensate for visual misalignment through hours and hours of practicing, where they

slowly learn to change their aim to compensate. Basketball players learn to aim a little more to the right or left. Young pitchers
learn where to look to place the ball in the right spot, though
eventually they may tend to find themselves moving out into the
field instead of pitching. Hockey and soccer players get a better
feel for aiming through repetitive practice. Another alternative is
exercise. The best exercise to help the eyes line up properly is the
Brock String exercise found in Chapter 12.

I'd like to mention that the method that I use for measuring an athlete's eye alignment for my ranking purposes is a little
more detailed and was developed by Dr. Craig L. Farnsworth
as described in his book *See It and Sink It: Mastering Putting
Through Peak Visual Performance.* This method comes up with a
measurement for the amount of misalignment that can be used
for comparative purposes. Elite athletes usually have perfectly
straight alignment.

In Front or Behind

One of the easiest ways to test if the eyes are aligned in front
of or behind an object is to use a string with a bead on it. The
athlete holds one end of the string up tight to his or her nose, and
the examiner holds the other end. The athlete is asked to look at
the hole of the bead that has been positioned in the middle of
the string and not to change her gaze. While the athlete is looking at the bead, it will appear to have two strings heading toward
it and two strings leaving it. The athlete will notice that the two
strings will appear to cross before, at, or behind the bead. If the
athlete has perfectly aligned horizontal vision, the two strings
will appear to cross at the bead.

For athletes with eye alignment that isn't as good, the strings
will appear to cross before or after the bead. Athletes who see

the string cross before the bead have eye alignment that is in front of the target. This means that they perceive the object to be closer than it really is. This will cause them to be short on shots and throws. They will react to objects before they actually get to them. Athletes who see the string cross after the bead have eye alignment that is behind the target. They perceive objects as farther away than they really are. They will throw basketballs up to the rim too hard, or they will react to a ball after it is past where they should have reacted (for example, they will swing late on a baseball that is pitched to them).

An easy test for alignment in front of or behind a target is by using a coin-toss test. Here, you place a quarter on the floor. Now, stand 10 feet away from the quarter with five dimes in your hand. Slowly toss one dime at a time at the quarter and record if you are short or long. (You can also record if you miss to the right or to the left, as in the tests for left or right misalignment.)

My observations of the coin-toss test are that the first throw gives you a very accurate finding of the spot of visual perception: in front of or behind the target. The second toss is usually a huge correction. In the third, fourth, and fifth tosses, the brain engages the rest of the body to compensate for the visual misalignment. You'll notice that these tosses will start close to where the first toss was and then each toss will walk slowly toward the quarter.

When athletes see the strings cross before the bead in the string test, or if the coin lands before the target, it means that their eyes align in front of the target and they will perceive things as being closer than they are in reality. Athletes whose eyes align behind the target see the strings cross behind the bead or throw the coins long; they perceive things as being farther away than they really are.

## Examples of Misalignment

Here are some examples of the tendencies that athletes demonstrate when their eyes are misaligned in front of or behind a target.

| If gaze is aligned in front of the target: | If gaze is aligned behind the target: |
|---|---|
| Football passes are thrown low | Football passes are thrown too high |
| Field-goal kicks are short | Field-goal kicks are long |
| Basketball players are short on their shots | Basketball players shoot long (throw bricks) or too hard |
| Baseball throws are more in the dirt | Baseball throws are too high |
| Hockey passes are short | Hockey shots go over the crossbar |
| Soccer shots and passes are short | Soccer shots go over the crossbar |
| Golfers are short on putts | Golfers are long on putts |
| Tennis players hit the net more than average | Tennis players hit the back line more than average |

## Up or Down

Again, when this type of misalignment is present, it's usually because of an injury to the eye socket that causes the actual eyeball to rest in a position lower than it should. Eye-muscle injury or paralysis can also cause this to occur. The best way to correct for these is through glasses known as "prisms" that have a special correcting property.

## Eye-Muscle Strength

Now that you know which eye to aim with and have learned if your eyes are pointed in the right direction, I'm going to teach you about how the eye muscles work and how to strengthen them. You can work out your eye muscles just like my daughter was doing with her biceps at the beginning of this chapter.

The mother of an eight-year-old boy had a question for me after I examined her son's eyes. "My husband has told Johnny not to cross his eyes because it's bad for him. Is that true?"

"No, that's not true," I explained. "Being able to cross your eyes is actually a good trait. Especially when it comes to sports."

Can you cross your eyes? Having the ability to cross one's eyes is a pretty basic skill. It's also a very important skill to have as an athlete.

Take the act of catching a ball, for instance. Your eyes are focused on the ball in another person's hand as he or she begins the throw. The person tosses the ball. The ball comes toward you. Your eyes target the ball as it moves in toward your hands. You catch the ball. If your eyes continued in the direction that they were moving to follow the ball, you would be looking at the tip of your nose soon and then at a spot even closer. This is what we mean by crossing your eyes. This motion of moving the eyes in toward the nose is known as *convergence*.

## Convergence and Convergence Insufficiency

Now try this. Can you cross your eyes and then keep your left eye in while you turn your right eye out toward your right ear? Next, can you bring your right eye back to look toward your nose and hold it in place while you turn your left eye out toward your left ear? Can you then bring your left eye back in and repeat the whole process?

Did you try to do the exercise? Have you ever seen anyone do this with his or her eyes? It's usually pretty funny to watch, but it is a great exercise. The person who can do this feat has great control of their eye muscles.

The eyes are just like two moving spotlights that are both highlighting the same actor on a stage. As the actor moves around, the spotlights have to move in unison to stay pointed at the actor. If the actor starts to run around and move faster, the spotlights have to work harder to keep up. As the degree of difficulty becomes greater, the chance of a spotlight being out of position—either lagging behind or overshooting the actor—becomes greater.

Your eyes are like the two spotlights that need to stay pointing at the same target. Each eye has six muscles that move it. The six muscles of the right eye have to be synchronized with the six muscles of the left eye. Each muscle has a range of motion, just like the muscles in other parts of our bodies. Each muscle has a certain strength and ability to move at various speeds.

Because the eyes are separated in space by an average of six centimeters, they each have a slightly different view of the world. This allows us to perceive things in three dimensions. Depth perception is very important in sports. It is achieved—and improved—by how well the two eyes work together as a team.

Here's a great way to demonstrate this to you. Stand about 20 feet away from a calendar and look at the first letter in the name of whatever month is showing. Continue to stare at that letter and place your right hand about three inches away from your face so that it's covering your right eye. Now swing it over to the front of your left eye while staying fixated on the same letter. Next, move your hand back over your right eye and then begin swinging it back and forth to alternately cover the eyes. You may notice that the letter begins to jump or move a little to the right or left and then back again. Some people will even notice that the letter jumps up and down a little bit as well.

For those of you who don't notice the letter jumping much

in the above exercise, your eyes are more closely aligned and are pointing where they should. For those of you who notice the letter jumping a little, your eyes are a little out of alignment. Those who notice a huge jump may have a larger misalignment.

*Fusion* is the term used to describe the ability of both eyes to point at a single object and send information to the brain so that only one image is seen and depth perception is noted. The eye muscles need to work to keep the image fused as it moves in space, instead of letting it split into two separate images, causing double vision. As an eye doctor, I measure the ability of the eyes to do this in a way that is similar to increasing the weights an athlete lifts with his or her arms. Often, it is the elite athletes who can lift the heaviest "eye muscle weights" with ease, and this gives us a standard for others to reach.

Since fusion is responsible for depth perception, both eyes have to have good vision and also have to work well together as a team for an athlete's depth perception to be good. In sports, fusion needs to be maintained not only when the gaze is straight ahead but at all areas of gaze. If not, depth perception will be lost and the athlete will begin to see double.

Eye doctors can run tests to measure a person's depth perception. These tests incorporate 3-D glasses and special books that have objects that seem to rise off of the page. Testing for depth perception in younger athletes is very important because it's one of the first exercises that gives the doctor a hint that both eyes aren't working together. I don't include depth-perception results in my ranking method because the high-caliber athletes who I rank all have great depth perception. However, I think that this measurement could be added to the ranking method that is found in Chapter 13 when it is used for younger athletes.

The first area in which the eyes tend to fall down on the

job when it comes to fusion is in the area of convergence. The inability to keep the eyes working together as an object comes toward us is the biggest culprit; this is known as *convergence insufficiency* or CI. The great news is that this is also the easiest problem to fix with eye exercises. Again, you can find several convergence exercises in Chapter 12 later in this book.

The easiest test to determine if an athlete can cross his or her eyes is known as a Pencil Push-Up. This is similar to the push-ups we do with our arms, only this drill is designed for the eyes. Grab a pencil and hold it straight ahead, at arm's length and pointing up. Slowly bring the pencil in while you concentrate your vision on the very tip of the pencil. You should be able to bring the pencil all the way in to touch your nose without it getting blurry and splitting into two (a double image).

Athletes with CI will start seeing two pencil tips as the pencil gets closer to the nose; they lose fusion. An athlete who has minor CI will be able to bring the pencil in to a point an inch or two away from the nose before losing fusion; the athlete with a deeper problem will notice the blur or double vision beginning three to four inches away from the nose, or even farther away. Although CI is one of the most common findings that I notice in athletes who are not reaching their full potential, it is also one of the easiest to train for improvement.

I started this chapter with the story of professional golfer Michael Campbell playing in the US Open and running to the bathroom every five holes or so. The specific problem that he experienced was with his right eye, which would not converge properly. He was going to the bathroom so that he could concentrate on the eye exercises he used to strengthen his convergence insufficiency. In these exercises, he used the tip of a tee to essentially perform the Pencil Push-Up exercise.

Up until now, I have only described convergence in terms of a straight-ahead gaze. But elite athletes can cross their eyes in different areas of gaze as well. Convergence in the next area of gaze is tested by having the athlete look up to evaluate their upward—or superior—gaze. To test this on yourself, keep your chin at its normal straight-ahead position and don't allow it to rise up. Now raise your hand up so that the pencil is about 18 inches higher than it was during the straight-ahead-gaze test. Again, look at the very tip of the pencil and bring it in a straight line toward your nose. Can you bring the tip in to touch your nose without it breaking into two images or blurring?

Let's talk about why it's important for athletes to have good convergence during upward gaze. Basketball players look up when they shoot. During a rebound, the ball comes off the rim or backboard toward an athlete. That athlete has to bring his eyes in toward his nose as he tracks the ball in for the catch.

If these athletes have CI on upward gaze, they have trouble tracking the ball as it travels toward a spot above their head. Their eyes will follow the ball in to the point where the eyes lose fusion. Then the ball will get blurry or double, and watch out! The player usually takes his or her eye off of the ball. I know you've heard that one: "Keep your eye on the ball!" Athletes with CI can only keep their eyes on the ball until the point of visual crisis, and then they have to change their gaze.

Now let's take a look at athletes who have the opposite problem. Some athletes have trouble bringing both eyes in together while looking down or using their downward gaze. To test convergence in downward or inferior gaze, you again use the Pencil Push-Up starting with the pencil at arm's length as you originally did to work on straight-ahead gaze. Now, move the pencil down about two feet, but keep your nose pointing straight ahead (in other words, don't drop your chin or head down). Bring the tip of the pencil from that downward position up to the tip of your nose while you are looking down at it.

A good example of when convergence in this lower gaze is important is the baseball player who is fielding a ground ball. He has to watch the ball as it leaves the bat, hits the ground, and then as it rolls toward him and comes all the way to his glove. Usually, the ball is moving fast and the athlete is running to a different location. The athlete who has a great visual system has an easier time keeping his eye on the ball.

The athlete with CI in lower gaze will have more trouble fielding that ground ball. The ball leaves the bat, hits the ground, rolls toward him and, as the eyes turn inward, they reach the point where they begin to lose fusion. The eyes can track the ball, but when it gets too close, the visual system reaches crisis and the player involuntarily takes an eye off the ball. The player then loses fixation on the ball or his depth perception becomes impaired and the ball dribbles between his legs. (I'm sure you've seen that one too!)

## Examples of CI

Examples of plays that can be problem areas for athletes with CI on upward or downward gaze include:

| CI on upward gaze: | CI on downward gaze: |
|---|---|
| A football receiver catching a pass | A football player trying to pick up a fumble |
| A football lineman looking up while in his stance | A football center looking at the ball to snap |
| A baseball player catching a fly ball | A baseball player fielding a ground ball |
| A baseball player who likes to hold his chin down while swinging to hit a ball | A baseball player who likes to raise his chin up while hitting |
| A soccer player heading a ball | A soccer player receiving a pass |
| A lacrosse player catching a high pass | A lacrosse player trying to get a ball that's rolling on the ground |
| A tennis player throwing the ball in the air for a serve | A tennis player hitting a low ball |
| A marksman following skeet | A hunter shooting from a tree stand |
| A volleyball player tracking the ball coming from above | A volleyball player trying to set the ball |
| A hockey goalie in a split reaching for a shot at the top of the net | A hockey player receiving a pass |

There are several eye exercises in both of the exercise chapters that help train convergence. The easiest exercises to start with are the Pencil Push-Up and Brock String exercises. I also like the Two Pennies Three exercise.

We just looked at the three areas of an athlete's gaze that I evaluate for convergence ability: straight-ahead gaze, upward gaze, and downward gaze. When I evaluate athletes for CI, I also try to give them a secondary classification of either *A*- or *V*- pattern CI. Eyes that converge well at upward gaze but that are CI on downward gaze are known as having an *A*-pattern weakness (representing the fact that the eyes are further apart on the bottom, just like the feet of the letter *A*). Eyes that work better on downward gaze and have CI at upward gaze are known as having *V*-pattern weakness (since the eyes are further apart up top).

Athletes with *A*-pattern weakness might start losing interest in sports that use downward gaze, such as soccer, and may move over to a sport such as volleyball. Their eyes work great looking up but are not so good looking down. Snowboarding and skateboarding are other activities that may be difficult for these athletes.

Athletes with *V*-pattern weakness may move away from baseball and football because of difficulty with convergence on the overhead catch and instead move to a sport such as soccer, which is dominated with more straight-ahead and downward gazes.

If you're working with athletes who can't bring their eyes in together fully and quickly, you now may be able to understand why both you and these athletes can become frustrated with their performance. This eye-muscle weakness has to be strengthened, or the rest of the athlete's development in the sport will be slower. As athletes progress up the ranks from elementary school age, these weaknesses in the visual system can start weeding athletes out of sports where their eyes just can't keep up.

---

*See to Play Tip 8:*
*Be able to cross your eyes high and low and*
*everywhere in between.*

Divergence and Divergence Insuffincency

Another problem that can occur with the eye muscles is that they may be sluggish when moving from near gaze to distance gaze. The muscles have to move the eyes from an inward to an outward position, which is known as *divergence*. If the muscles are sluggish in this task, the athlete has divergence insufficiency (DI).

An example of how DI can affect an athlete is the baseball catcher who catches the ball and tries to throw out a player stealing second base. The catcher sees the ball in to his glove, then looks up to find the second baseman. When the eyes are slow to focus at that spot in the distance, the throw will bounce short because that is where the eyes are pointing. To fix this, the athlete does exercises to learn how to relax the muscles of the visual system.

**Eye Tracking**

While you read this book, your eye muscles guide your eyes smoothly along the line that these words are on so you can read them clearly. Once you get to the end of this line you shift the eyes back to the next line to continue reading. This is an example of a coordinated eye movement that eye doctors call *eye tracking* or *pursuits*. The eye muscles have to perform this task in a smooth and uniform manner or your vision will become jumpy. As an eye doctor, I test everyone for eye movement and tracking ability. If I notice that people have trouble performing these tasks, I can recommend exercises to help them overcome these problems.

When people move their eyes from object to object, the eyes usually jump straight to the target with no problem. Some people's eyes may move in a more spastic motion and either overshoot or undershoot the object. This is a different issue than the eye-alignment problems described earlier, in that the alignment may be fine once they get their eyes to the right position. However, it's hard for them to get the eyes to the right spot with a single smooth eye movement. They may have to move the eyes a second time to get to the correct spot. The action of the eyes jumping from one target to another is called a *saccade*. There are standard tests that eye doctors use to test how well people can use their eyes to jump from target to target.

**Get Moving!**

Now that we've defined convergence and divergence issues and problems with eye movement and tracking, let's take care of them. We'll do it like we do any other weaknesses with muscles in the body: Exercise! Get your eyes moving!

Eye doctors and vision therapists use eye exercises to help the eye muscles work better and to help the eyes work better as a team. *Vision therapy* is the term that most people use when referring to this type of eye-muscle training. I use vision therapy for children who have vision problems that interfere with learning, such as CI and DI. I even have exercises that I'll discuss later in this book that help with focusing, which in turn can help people work better and longer on computers and when reading.

The sports-vision therapy that I use with elite athletes goes a step further by incorporating sport-specific training into these eye exercises. The visual demands on the eye muscles of athletes during their normal workday are far greater than the visual demands on the average person's eye muscles at work. Athletes who play visually demanding sports are actually performing eye-muscle exercises just by practicing their sports. I recommend additional and sport-specific training for athletes to do at home or in my office to help provide them with additional ways to exercise these muscles and even target specific eye muscles. This is similar to the way that weightlifting or strength training helps athletes isolate and strengthen specific muscle groups. This type of eye exercising can help the eye muscles reach their fullest potential.

I have included eye-muscle exercises in my exercise chapters, but a brief discussion is warranted here so that this section of the book makes the maximum of sense.

The first place to start is with the warm-up. For the eyes, warming up the eye muscles is pretty easy stuff. Stand or sit 20 feet from a wall. Look at the top left-hand corner. Now, move your eyes—just your eyes, not your head—to trace an imaginary line across the top of the wall like you are looking at a line of words on a page, but do it with speed. When you get to the end of the line, zig back to the left, a little lower down, and repeat. Follow this zigzag pattern all the way to the ground and then zigzag in reverse back to the top. Do this about three times, and then continue to warm up with rotations. Rotations consist of tracing large circles with your eyes or rolling your eyes. Start by doing a clockwise rotation a couple of times, and then move counterclockwise a couple times. You can mix and match the patterns and should work your eyes for one to two minutes. Now you are warmed up!

The first convergence exercise is the same procedure we used to test the eyes earlier in this chapter; the Pencil Push-Up. You perform this exercise in all three areas of gaze. Start with the easiest position of gaze for your eyes and end with the hardest position of gaze. That means, for example, that the *A*-pattern athlete starts with upward gaze. Hold the pencil in the upward position at arm's length and bring it toward you until it begins to double. Try to keep fusion at that point and then move the pencil back out to arm's length. Bring it slowly back in to the point where fusion begins to be lost. The goal is to work up to bringing the pencil completely in to touch your nose without causing blurred or double vision at any point. Do this exercise 10 times and then move to straight-ahead gaze. This is where the pencil is held at arm's length and level with your nose. Begin the exercise by slowly bringing the pencil in until the vision blurs or becomes double and then move it back out to arm's length. Exercise this area of gaze 10 times as well. Now, go to downward gaze. Remember, with the $A$ pattern, exercising convergence in downward gaze will be hardest. Hold the pencil at arm's length in the downward-gaze position and slowly move it toward your nose until you begin to see double. Again, try to maintain fusion and slowly move it back out. Then, bring it back in, working to bring it closer without losing fusion, until you can eventually touch your nose. You should do this 10 times as well. I recommend that you perform this exercise for about five to eight minutes, so you may have to start again from the beginning a couple of times. This exercise can also cause a whopping headache the first few times you do it, which is similar to the burn other muscles feel when lifting weights.

I call the next exercise the Near-Point Jump. You again start with the easiest area of gaze depending on the $A$ or $V$ pattern. With the $A$ pattern, you start with the pencil pointing tip down and held at a spot about three inches from your forehead. Focus on the pencil tip so that it is clear and then dart your eyes across the room to the top of a wall that is at least 15 feet away. Then dart your eyes back to the pencil tip. Pencil, wall, pencil, wall, etc. Repeat this for 60 seconds. Now, move to straight-ahead gaze, with the pencil tip three inches directly in front of your eyes, and do the same for 60 seconds. End by exercising down-ward gaze for 60 seconds. Here the pencil tip will be pointing upward and at chin level about one to two inches from the face but far enough so that it is not blocked by your nose.

These two exercises give you an idea of how to work on improving the visual system's convergence ability. As I mentioned earlier, you will find even more exercises that work to improve eye movement later in this book. Exercises that can be particularly helpful to young athletes are provided in the Early Exercises chapter as well.

As we've discussed, elite athletes often have better acuity and a zone of great vision that encompasses a larger area than that of average athletes. In this chapter, we've learned that elite athletes' eye muscles point their eyes with more accuracy and allow for better eye movement.

So get to it! Get your eye muscles moving!

# CHAPTER 5
## FAST FOCUS FINISHES FIRST

Elite athletes see everything clearly. Their eyes have great acuity for the tiniest of details, even at a distance. They can bring the letters on this page into focus even if it is held one inch from their eyes. They can focus on objects that shift from left to right and from far to near. They can focus on a puck flying toward them from the side or on a football that pops into view 15 feet away as it floats from behind them, over a shoulder and into their fingertips. They can see the seams of a fastball as it is pitched to determine the rotation of the ball, focus in on a fast-moving tennis ball as it hits the racquet or on a soccer ball spinning toward them as they get ready to make a pass with their heads.

The ability to focus clearly is one of the most important aspects of vision in sports and for learning in school. Any decrease in this ability can wreak havoc on the playing field or in the classroom.

Carolina Hurricanes forward Sergei Samsonov gave me a great example of how important it is for an athlete to be able to focus clearly. During the 2010–11 season he sustained a concussion during a game that bothered his visual system. He felt it wasn't a big issue, and he could perform most of the tasks he needed to on the ice while he was rehabilitating. But he also felt that something was "a bit off" about his game. I evaluated him and found that the focusing system in his left eye wasn't working properly. We did some focusing exercises in the office that day.

Sergei's focusing system responded almost immediately and his symptoms disappeared.

In the previous chapter, you learned the importance of using the correct eye for aiming, pointing both eyes to the same spot so that your brain can combine the two images into one, and moving the eyes as a team in order to keep the images fused. In this chapter I will talk about the mechanism that works to change and dial in the details of an object so that we see it clearly.

There is a lens in each of our eyes that is located behind the colored part of the eye (the *iris*). This lens is very similar to a lens in a camera in that it has to move to focus clearly on the details of an object. As I described in the previous chapter, your eyes are converged or pointed in while looking at the words on this page; they are moving along in a fashion that allows you to read, but it is the lens inside each eye that moves or dials in the appropriate amount to help you see the letters clearly. If your lenses did not focus, you would still see the words on the page, but they would be very blurry and you would not be able to distinguish their meaning. The lens system is completely relaxed when we look at things in the distance and has to work harder as it focuses on images that are closer to the body. The act of this focusing is called *accommodation*.

There are two aspects of the lens system that I will talk about in this chapter. First is the strength of the lens system. Just like an athlete can bench-press a certain amount of weight, the lens system has to be able to have a certain amount of strength in order to focus on images. Lens-system strength is a function of the flexibility of the actual lens (which is predetermined and cannot be changed) and the strength of the muscles that move it (which can be strengthened with exercises, just like other muscles in the body). The second thing I will discuss is the speed and accuracy of the lens system. In sports, any focusing action has to be done fast and accurately; the lens system cannot overshoot or undershoot on the amount of focus it needs to provide.

In this day and age of digital phones and cameras, I can give you an illustration of how the focusing system of the eye works. The lens in an eye is just like the lens in a camera; it has to zoom in and out to keep images clear as they move closer and farther away from us. These days, most of the lenses in cameras are automatic and controlled by an internal system. The lenses in our eyes are also run by an internal system of tiny muscles that allow them to focus.

Santa Claus brought my wife a great new camera for Christmas. She had studied up on different types of cameras and asked Santa for this particular one because its lens was ranked as one of the best for focusing on objects at a long distance. When we attended my oldest daughter's high school graduation, we had to sit so far away from the stage that we felt like we were in the next county. When it was finally my daughter's turn to go across the stage, shake the superintendent's hand, and get her diploma, I was able to zoom in with the camera and capture the moment almost perfectly. The picture was so good that it was similar to a picture taken by the camera used by a professional photographer only 20 feet from the stage.

I turned quickly to my family sitting right beside me and pushed the button again to refocus the lens of the camera. The camera made a humming sound as the lens readjusted to focus up close, and I took a clear picture of them at the proud moment of my daughter becoming a graduate.

The camera responded nicely. It didn't hesitate in either moment. I was able to take a clear picture of my daughter in the next county and I was able to take a clear picture of my family sitting three feet away from me. So there are two points about my wife's camera that I am trying to illustrate:

1. It can zoom in and out with great precision.
2. It does this with a certain amount of speed.

The camera that is built in to my cell phone is a different story. I love it. I'm a big fan of taking pictures and emailing them to my family. But the camera lens in my phone does not have nearly the capability or the same traits of my wife's camera.

If you're an athlete and were told you could choose to have eyes that focus like my wife's camera versus my cell phone, I'm sure you'd choose the camera, so that your eyes could zoom in and out with strength and great speed. I think you can just imagine how much harder it would be to focus on a ball moving at a fast speed toward you if your focusing system was more limited like the camera in my phone.

Let's break down the functioning of how an eye focuses. Picture yourself sitting on a slightly reclined chair at a beautiful sandy beach on a warm, sunny day. You are relaxing with a favorite book on your lap as you gaze out over the ocean listening to the sound of the waves as they come to the shore. Your eyes are pointed straight ahead, viewing the horizon where the sky meets the ocean. At this particular point, the lens has a skinny, convex shape to it and the muscles that move it to focus are completely relaxed. Now, you decide to read your book. The muscles of the eyes turn your eyeballs inward so that they are pointing at the book. But the letters are blurry. Your brain notices that the letters are blurry, so it sends out a message to the focusing mechanism, and the muscles around the lens move, causing it to bulge so that it gets fatter in the middle, and the letters you are reading begin to come in clearer.

The work of the muscles that move the lens to focus on an object that is close to the body requires a certain amount of strength and is similar to the work of the muscles of the chest and arms when we are doing push-ups. Throughout the day, as we do more and more near work, like reading or working on the computer, the focusing system can get tired, sluggish, and even begin to give us headaches. Athletes' focusing systems get a similar workout because they are constantly focusing on objects that are near to them.

Besides the strength of the muscles that help the lens focus, the other factor to look at in an athlete's ability to focus is how quickly a shift occurs from focus on a near object to a far object. I call this the "shift of focus." This represents the speed at which athletes can focus the lenses of their eyes to the proper level so that they can see an object clearly as it moves, such as the seams of a baseball during a pitch.

Elite athletes can bring their focusing system to the maximum level (strength of focus), and they can do it faster than others (shift of focus).

The problem is that some athletes' eyes just don't focus as well as others'. I measure the physical traits of the focusing system for each athlete I examine in order to determine how well it is working. I use these measurements as part of my visual ranking system to compare athletes.

**Strength of Focus**

In the eye doctor's office, there are machines that can measure the amount of focusing the eye muscles can perform. I have athletes look through the lenses in a machine at small letters on a chart about 16 inches away. Players are told to keep the letters clear at all times, and I slowly start changing the lenses to deliberately make it harder for athletes to focus. In this way, I test how much focusing strength they have or the amount of "eye weights" they can lift. Each click of the machine is like adding a weight to the focusing muscles and the amount of work the eyes have to do to keep the image clear. Eventually, each athlete gets to the point where I have added so much weight that the focusing system can't keep up and the eye can no longer bring the image into focus. This point gives us a way of measuring and comparing the strength of the focusing mechanism (known as the *amplitude of accommodation*, which is recorded in units known as diopters).

Because each eye has its own focusing mechanism, I test the right eye first, the left eye second, and then both eyes together. This helps me determine if one eye is having more of an issue than the other or if there is a problem with both eyes working as a team. Since every eye is different, I do expect the results of the right- and left-eye focus tests to be a little different. A large difference between the two eyes means that there probably is a focusing issue.

Depending on the sport, an athlete's strength of focus may not make a difference in the competition. Sometimes it can be the deciding factor in how the athlete performs. Athletes who are found to have deficiencies in accommodation can perform exercises to improve their focusing ability. These exercises are similar to strengthening the arms and chest by doing push-ups, only they target the muscles of the focusing mechanism. The Book/ Calendar Scan in the exercise chapter is used for this purpose.

One other thing to note here is that the cells inside the lens are constantly changing through the aging process. Over time, the lens becomes physically fatter and harder to move; it loses its flexibility. As a result, there are age-appropriate maximum focusing levels that decrease over time. Just as most athletes have slowed down on their 40-yard dash time at the age of 50 compared to the age of 20, the focusing of the lenses in the eyes also slows down. This change is known as *presbyopia*. No procedure has been developed to extend the life of the focusing mechanism (that is, there is no magic pill or fountain of youth to keep us focusing like when we were young).

The term for the focusing system not having enough strength to focus is called *accommodation insufficiency*. A child who has accommodation insufficiency usually is a slower reader, if he or she chooses to read at all. These children will also avoid staying on task for other near-point activities because they can't make the near image clear. They have the tendency to flit around, never settling on one task. (Care has to be taken not to label these children as having an attention-span problem when they really have an eye-focusing problem.) These children may also have the tendency to prop their heads up with one arm on a bent elbow, almost covering one eye, to let the eye that has better focusing ability do more of the work. These children may also rub their eyes significantly after reading for a while.

Accommodation insufficiency is the number one focusing issue that I find in children, and it's also the number one focusing issue with athletes. This is the reason that I test the strength of the focusing mechanism early and often in young athletes. Good focusing helps make better student athletes through elementary, middle, and high school. Students who build stronger focusing systems have more visual stamina, which can help them perform better for longer stretches of time, such as during testing in school, instead of burning out. Their focusing systems can build the proper strength to handle their reading workload.

Most sports activities inherently help train weaknesses in focusing as the child athlete is developing. Think of the simple game of pitch-and-catch. The child throws the ball to someone and watches it being caught. Next, the person throws the ball to the child, who focuses on it as it's flying through the air toward him or her and watches it into the glove or hand. This happens over and over, forcing the muscles of the lens system to work harder to focus as the ball comes closer and then release as the ball gets further away. You will find exercises in this book that suggest writing letters and numbers on balls that can be read while they are being tossed. Focusing on a letter or progression of letters as the ball moves through the air forces us to use the focusing system properly.

**Shift of Focus**

*Shift of focus* refers to how fast the focusing system shifts the lens into the correct shape to view objects clearly as they travel from far to near. Everything is usually moving fast in the athlete's world. Athletes' focusing systems have to adjust quickly so that they can see clearly and then readjust as they shift focus to another object.

Why is shift of focus so important in sports? I'll use baseball to illustrate this point. When the hitter is watching the pitch, he focuses on the ball in the pitcher's hand to see how the fingers are holding the ball. As the ball flies to the plate, the hitter watches to see how its seams are rotating. He needs to know both how the pitcher holds the ball and then how the ball rotates in the air to know what type of pitch was thrown so that he can hit the ball successfully. Another example is the player who has to field a line-drive grounder hit to him in the infield. He focuses on the speeding ball as it moves into his glove, then has to look up and focus on the first baseman's glove to throw the ball to the correct spot.

Eye doctors test to determine if the focusing system is shifting from near to far correctly. I test this for most people by using four lenses that are mounted on a lens holder. Two convex lenses are paired together, and when you look through them at reading material, the focusing system has to relax for the words to be seen clearly. The other two paired lenses are concave, and they force the focusing system to work in order to make the words clear. These are called +/- flippers because they get flipped back and forth to shift the focusing system from working to relaxing. I do this test for one minute with around 15 cycles of these flips. This test is also a good way to exercise our shift of focus as well as increase the focusing mechanism's strength.

```
See to Play Tip 9:
Fast focus finishes first.
```

The test of the focusing system that I use when I rank athletes is a little more competitive than the flipper test and results in a score that I can use to compare athletes to each other directly.

I call this test the Speed-Focus Read. It requires a stopwatch and 40 cards from a deck of playing cards with normal-sized print split up into two piles of 20. The athlete holds one pile of the cards with the print face down, about 16 inches from his nose and at a level even with his belly button. The test administrator stands 15 feet away with a stopwatch and the other pile of cards face down as well. The tester states the age-old, "On your mark, get set, go!" and starts timing the test. The athlete turns up the first card from the deck in his hands, reads it, and throws it to the floor. The tester shows the first card on the top of her pile at the level of the athlete's eyes. After the athlete reads the distant card, he turns up and reads the next card in the pile that he is holding. The athlete continues reading the cards in this near, then far, then near fashion until all the cards have been read. As soon as the athlete recognizes the last card available, the tester records the time. This time represents the shift-of-focus time. The quickest time I've seen is 20.4 seconds. Elite athletes tend to score in the 20- to 22-second range. You can score for accuracy as well with this test by setting the cards up in a specific sequence that can be repeated each time.

Just as the flipper test doubles as an exercise, the Speed-Focus Read is a great exercise. A variation called the Card Toss is found in Chapter 12.

The different conditions that interfere with the focusing—or accommodative—system that I can measure and recommend exercises to improve are:

- Accommodative insufficiency (not enough focusing)
- Accommodative infacility (sporadic focusing)
- Accommodative excess (overfocusing on objects)
- Accommodative lock (focusing that gets stuck)

There are plenty of exercises included in this book to help athletes get their focusing systems working better. Again, I'd like to state that sometimes the focusing system of one eye is affected more than the other, and care needs to be taken to do the exercises in proper order.

To that point, many of the exercises can be performed to isolate the weaker eye by using an eye patch to cover the stronger eye. This is similar to exercising one arm more if it is weaker than the other. By patching the strong eye, the weak eye is targeted for individual training. This variation on the exercises can help build the ability of the weaker eye to shift focus and also improve strength of focus.

As the weaker eye improves, the athlete can start exercising with both eyes open but with a continuing emphasis on that weaker eye. Eye doctors have machines, glasses, and prisms that can be used to isolate the eye that is being exercised. For example, athletes can wear red/green glasses or 3-D glasses to allow each eye to train separately while they are both open. Athletes feel like they are seeing with both eyes simultaneously, but they are actually seeing different things with each eye. This type of training allows each eye to work individually even though both eyes are open, thus allowing the trainer to target the weaker eye for more work. This approach increases the difficulty level over exercises done with a completely closed or patched eye.

Eye injuries can impair the focusing mechanism as well. This will be discussed in greater detail in Chapter 10. If the muscles and lens are injured with blunt trauma, focusing ability can decrease. Brain injuries sustained in concussions can also alter how an athlete focuses.

I'll finish this chapter by just restating that problems with our focusing mechanism are the most common problems I find with athletes. This, in my opinion, makes it a major obstacle that can keep them from reaching their genetic potential. It's also one of the most common culprits keeping our kids from becoming good scholastic athletes.

Because these issues are easily improved through proper vision exercise, it is imperative to catch these issues early in life so these kids can see to learn and see to play.

# CHAPTER 6
## EYE-HAND-BODY COORDINATION

I'm going to start this chapter by putting you in the following situation: You love being an official timer at swim meets. You started by volunteering at your local pool while your kids were swimming for the swim team and found that you had a knack for running the stopwatch. You began volunteering for high school meets and year-round swim clubs. You became well known for your professionalism through national events. One day you got a call from the International Olympic Committee; you were selected as an official timer for the 2008 Beijing Summer Olympics.

The games have started, and you have a good feel for the flow of your task, starting with pushing the stopwatch when you see the flash of the starter's light and hear the sound of the *beep* that starts the race, then following the swimmer in your lane, and finally pushing the button when that swimmer's hand hits the wall. You look at the time on your stopwatch, write it down on an official timer's form, and turn it in to the judges.

The 100-meter men's butterfly event is ready to begin. You look down. *Wow*, you think. You are the timer for USA swimmer Michael Phelps.

"Swimmers, take your mark," the announcer says, followed by the flash and *beep*. They're off!

You've started your stopwatch, and things are moving well. Here comes the end of the race. Oh, my golly, it's a close one. Here comes Michael. He hits the wall. You push the stopwatch button. His time from your watch is one one-hundredth (0.01) of a second faster than the second-place swimmer. He wins the gold medal! What a rush!

A few races later, you find yourself getting ready to time the 50-meter women's freestyle race. You look to find the swimmer in your lane and, lo and behold, this time you are in charge of timing USA swimmer Dara Torres.

"Swimmers, take your mark," the announcer says, followed by the flash and *beep*. They're off!

You've started your stopwatch, and life is good. Here the swimmers come. Wow, it's another very close race! Dara's hand hits the wall. You push your button. Oh no! She's one one-hundredth of a second behind the fastest swimmer. She's lost the gold! Why so close again? Were you as accurate as you could have been? Was her loss your fault?

The races and actual time results are real in the above stories. But the human stopwatch timing was not. The timing was left up to electronic timers. Humans, it turns out, aren't as accurate. So you are off the hook as far as pushing the stopwatch button too slowly!

I use this situation to start our discussion on eye-hand-body coordination to illustrate how important reaction time is in sports. Many of you who have played sports understand this already. A split second can alter the outcome of a play and ultimately the outcome of a game. *Eye-hand-body coordination* is the act of the athlete's eye seeing something, the brain deciding the proper response to it, and the movement of a hand or body part in reaction to that stimulus. It's no stretch to say that elite athletes do these tasks better than average athletes. This is what helps make them elite.

I'm sure it makes sense when I say that some athletes have

better eye-hand coordination than other athletes. Eye doctors have machines to test athletes for eye-hand reaction time and eye-hand coordination. These tests give us results that allow for comparisons between athletes. I also use exercises to help athletes who are weaker in this area improve.

Getting back to our stopwatch story, a study performed on human and electronic timing showed that human timing, on average, had a delay of between 0.18 and 0.23 seconds at the beginning of a race and a delay of between 0.11 and 0.15 seconds at the finish. The smaller difference in the finish delay than in the start delay suggests that we use some form of anticipation or projection of the hand hitting the wall at the end of a race when deciding to push the timer button, as opposed to the cold start at the beginning of the event. This begins to show us that eye-hand-body coordination is not purely just a reaction but that there is some component of learned or trained response that helps the brain get the body reacting quicker, especially in sports.

In the previous chapters, you learned about how the eyes work in order to see to play, and now I'm going to expand into how the visual system talks to the brain, how the brain uses that information, and how the brain directs the body to get moving to perform the resulting action. I'll discuss how this sequence goes through stages:

- Instinctive, reactive response (we react reflexively)
- Thought process-evoked response (we think about the action and make it happen)
- Trained response that develops into reflexive response (we practice, practice, practice until the response is a reaction that we no longer have to think about to perform)

I'll start by breaking down the systems of the body and brain into basic pieces and showing how they are tied together and interact with each other. I think this will help later when I discuss how fine-tuned these systems become in elite athletes.

Let's talk computers. How many times a day do you interact with something that has a computer or artificial brain in it? You get up in the morning and turn on the television for the morning news. Most of the cable boxes and satellite boxes have a small computer to help the box function. You check your cell phone, a minicomputer, for messages. You turn on your PC to check your email. You play a tune on your iPod, another minicomputer. You go out and turn on the car, which has minicomputers to help it run. You get to work, and there's another computer to turn on. You get the idea. There are computers in most parts of our daily lives, but the only master computer that hooks them all together is us.

For the large number of minicomputers in your body, your nervous system is the master computer. The minicomputers take in information about what's going on out there, and the nervous system takes control over deciding how to react to that information and, in general, telling the body how to get things done. The nervous system has two parts:

- The *voluntary nervous system* (or somatic nervous system) gives you conscious control over your actions and motions. We often think of this part of the system as "the brain."
- The *involuntary nervous system* (or autonomic nervous system) keeps your body running by controlling your heart, breathing, and other body functions without you having to do anything.

The eyes are a camera, an input device to the nervous system, that take in information about what we see. The voluntary nervous system absorbs the visual information from the eyes and acts on it and may also store it in our memory banks for future reference. So if in basketball we see an opponent with the ball do a "juke" to start to shoot, our brains tell our bodies, "It's truly a shot, and we'd better jump up to try to block it!" or, "We've seen that before and that move is a fakeout—don't believe it!" Another input device, called *proprioception*, has many parts scattered throughout the body that provide information that helps your nervous system determine your body's orientation in space and time.

## Instinctive Reflexive Responses

Let's look at the most basic pathway between the eyes and the brain, which is the "see it and react without thought" reflex.

In this most basic reflex, also called the "blink" or "menace reflex," the eyes relay information to the brain indicating harm and danger, which initiates a protective reflex. This reflex is an important part of our fight-or-flight response to danger. The eye is no dummy; it wants to protect itself first. So when we see something flying toward our eyes, we blink. This is an instinctive response; in other words, it does not require us to use our brains to think about the response.

It takes a tenth of a second for the eye to blink when something is coming toward it. The eye "camera" takes a picture of something flying toward it. It sends a picture along the blink-reflex pathway to the brain, which doesn't have to think, *Oh no! There is something that is going to hit me! I need protection! Shut that eyelid.* Instead, impulses are sent out immediately to the lid, and the lid closes in order to protect the eye. You would have to imagine that this process would be the quickest and most basic eye-to-brain-to-body response that our bodies perform.

This is one of the reasons that race-car drivers have problems with dry eyes. They've trained their blink reflexes to relax so they don't blink as much, and as a result their corneas dry out more. Why have they conditioned themselves to do that? As you just learned, the blink of an eye takes a tenth of a second. Imagine yourself as a NASCAR driver at the Daytona 500 or as an Indianapolis 500 race-car driver, driving at about 200 miles an hour. Something hits your windshield or visor, and you blink. During the tenth of a second that it took you to blink, your car traveled almost 30 feet. You just have to hope that while you are blinking, nothing gets into your path for the next 30 feet, or you are going to hit it. So training to stop or ease up your blink reflex is a survival technique to keep you from crashing your car. The unintended side effect of not blinking is dry eyes.

The second most basic involuntary way the brain uses visual input is by feeding information into the proprioception system, which is in charge of letting the body know about orientation in space, movement, and balance. This system includes vision, the inner ear, and sensors on muscles and joints in our body. Have you ever been sitting in a parked car and all of a sudden been startled because the car feels like it's moving? You look around and realize that the car in the parking space next to you is the one moving and your car is still parked. Your vision just faked out your proprioception system. This happens at the IMAX theater when you are watching a movie and actually feel like you are flying or falling. This is another example of the dorsal visual stream at work (which we talked about in Chapter 3).

**Thought Process-Evoked Responses**

Now, let's talk about the process of your brain taking in visual information, making a decision, and starting a response based on that decision. How long does it take to process the sight of a fastball coming toward you, get the image sent to your brain, have your brain think through, *Oh, it's a fastball, and it's moving over to this spot. Let's move the hands, arms, rotate the body...now!* and then send those impulses out in a coordinated fashion so that all the right parts of your body react? Or how long does it take the picture of a puck to get from your eyes to the brain, so that the brain thinks, *Oh, there's the puck, there's the net...it's an open man! Let's move the arms to get that stick to hit the puck...now!* and then passes on impulses to make the body move to shoot and score? Or your eye takes a picture of a fierce tackler getting ready to cream you because you've got the ball. The eye sends the message to the brain, the brain digests the message and screams, *Oh no!!* Next, your brain sends out impulses so that your body reacts and you avoid the tackle and score a touchdown.

The easiest place to start the discussion of eye-hand-body reaction time would be by a breakdown of hitting a 90-mph fastball. This movement has been analyzed and broken down in several books and articles by other authors, so I'm just going to give you the basic idea. The time that it takes for the ball to leave the pitcher and get to the plate is four-tenths of a second. From the start of the pitch, it takes the batter's eye one-tenth of a second to see the ball and send the message to the brain. The next tenth of a second is used to determine the flight of the ball and type of pitch, whether deciding to swing the bat, or not, and finally where to put the bat head. Then it takes a little over two-tenths of a second to send the message to all the body parts needed to swing and hit the ball to the right location. The faster the pitch, the more important the batter's ability to predict and project where the ball will arrive. The slower the pitch, the more accurate the swing can be because the hitter has more time to involve the brain in making the decision and responding to the pitch. This thought process is pretty similar to that of our stopwatch story since both impact the time it takes us to react.

Hopefully you're starting to understand that the normal untrained eye-hand reaction time is two-tenths of a second. If you're at the fair or Chuck E. Cheese's and you start playing Whac-A-Mole, it's going to take you roughly two-tenths of a second per mole unless you start using some type of anticipation move.

When we get the legs involved or use many coordinated body moves, it may take more than two-tenths of a second. Some literature has shown that a lower-body reaction—in a sport like soccer, for instance—may take up to three-tenths of a second.

Now use that two-tenths-of-a-second rule and imagine yourself as a NASCAR or Indianapolis 500 race-car driver traveling 200 miles per hour. You have enough time and space to react to anything that happens more than 59 feet in front of your car. If a rabbit runs on the track 61 feet away from you, he's safe. If he's in your way at 58 feet, you won't be able to steer clear. Also remember, if you blink right as the rabbit comes on the track, you'll use up to 30 feet during the blink of your eye.

**Trained Reflexive Responses**

There are two ways in which your conscious brain can react to visual information: with an evoked response that is the result of a thought process or with a trained reflexive response. The evoked response occurs when our eyes send information to our brains and we consciously make a decision based on that information. A trained reflexive response develops through repetitive practice. Conscious thought begins to be taken out of the equation because our bodies develop a feel for the proper response. Eye-hand-body reaction time improves as this reflex-type action develops.

When we break down the thought process of a batter trying to hit a 90-mph pitch, it looks like there is really no time to spare, doesn't it? But most hitters have practiced so many hours in their lives that they have been able to turn some of the art and science of hitting a baseball into a trained reflex. They have seen all the different types of pitches that pitchers throw. They have watched the different arm motions that pitchers use for each type of pitch. They have studied the fingers on the ball to see the different ways in which the pitcher holds it and releases it to cause a certain spin specific to that type of pitch. They have read scouting reports on the pitchers so they are familiar with each pitcher's best two or three pitches. They can project where the ball will go and anticipate where to put the bat to hit the ball at the right spot. Anticipation, projection, and repetitive muscle memory help them reduce the reaction time needed to hit the ball.

By the way, pitchers also study hitters. They know which pitches each hitter has a harder time hitting or evaluating. The pitchers who throw the ball slower look to add more movement to the ball, up or down or from left and right, and work on change-up speeds. Faster pitchers work very hard on making the mechanics of their arms during a throw look the same on all pitches, causing the hitter to see the same arm action on a fastball, slider, curveball, breaking ball, change-up, knuckleball, etc., making it less likely that the batter will know what pitch is coming next. (From an eye doctor's standpoint, it is truly fascinating watching the battle of pitcher versus hitter. It's mano a mano at its finest!)

Tennis is another visually tough sport. Here, the ball speed during the serves exceeds even the fastest baseball pitch. The fastest serve on record was over 150 miles per hour. This gives no time for mental decision-making. The athlete has to use anticipation and projection to react in time.

Athletes use anticipation and projection to shave time from their total reaction time. Through repetition, actions become more of a reflex instead of a consciously thought-out act. Again, this is the same explanation for why the human timers have less of a delay hitting the stopwatch at the end of the swimming races than at the beginning—they anticipate and project when each swimmer's hand is going to touch the wall.

Athletes learn to take in visual clues to shave down reaction time and to improve the speed of their eye-hand-body responses. As a matter of fact, it's suggested that through the years of practicing their respective sports, athletes catalog mental pictures of their eye-hand-body reactions that allow them to get to a spot quicker. A great example of reducing eye-hand-body reaction time using these factors is the faceoff in ice hockey. Two athletes face each other at a given faceoff spot. A referee stands between them with the puck in his hand and waits until the athletes are situated and stationary. The referee then drops the puck on the faceoff spot to begin play. The players move their sticks to gain control of the puck and direct it to a teammate to start the given play. One team has an offensive play ready to get the puck to the goal to score. The other team has a defensive play to get the puck out of their zone and down the ice toward their own goal so that they can score. The player who successfully hits the puck to his or her team when it drops is deemed the winner of the faceoff.

In the National Hockey League, there is a statistic to track the percentage of times a player wins faceoffs that is used to compare athletes with each other. Rod Brind'Amour of the Carolina Hurricanes was among the leaders in the NHL in winning faceoff percentages for many of the years he played. I spoke with him about what he felt made him one of the best faceoff athletes in the business and what things he attributed to helping him maintain his consistent high rate of success in winning faceoffs.

He explained to me that winning the faceoff draw is more involved than just the eye-hand reaction time of watching the puck drop. In most faceoffs, there is a routine that is performed. The players and referee move to the faceoff spot. The referee motions to the visiting team's player to step in toward the spot. Then, the home-team player is motioned in toward the spot. Everyone settles down. The referee shows the puck to the visiting player, then the home-team player, and then the puck is slightly lifted and dropped. Rod said that if this routine is followed, he can usually win the draw hands down because he has developed a great feel for the whole timing and flow of the routine. (However, in this faceoff mode any player who tries to anticipate the referee dropping the puck but swats too early toward the faceoff spot will get thrown out of the faceoff circle almost as though they're being told, "You're trying to cheat.")

Rod also explained to me that in some games the referees don't use the above routine and instead just come in and drop the puck. This process results in more of a free-for-all. In this faceoff mode you will see players start swatting their sticks immediately as they get into the faceoff circle, and they won't get thrown out of the circle. So in this second example, trained eye-hand-body reaction is replaced by guessing and swatting an opponent's stick out of the way and getting rewarded. Rod told me that in this type of faceoff mode, he felt he was less predictable in winning the draw, as were most players, and it was more of a 50/50 chance that he would win.

You can start to see with this example of a faceoff that the athlete is beginning to trust instincts that have been trained. In the above instance, Rod used to think about every faceoff, but somewhere along the way, it became a trained, instinctual response (at least when the ref used the more predictable ritual). He picked up on the visual clues and started taking his brain out of the conscious thought mode of, *Go! Move your stick.* Instead, the decision was being made by a reflex action that he had developed.

Let's switch gears a bit by mathematically plotting out the vision's role in a pass play in football. The quarterback is going to throw the ball 60 miles per hour to me as the receiver. I am running a 10-yard curl-in pattern. I line up 15 yards from the ball, where it's snapped. He drops back four yards to throw. I run my 10-yard pattern. He releases the ball. Theoretically, the ball is going to travel a little over 20 yards in the air. The airtime travel for the ball from his release is a little over six-tenths of a second. Visually, I would have to spot the ball around six yards away from me in order to have enough time to catch it. (Now, since I am nearsighted and I play without glasses or contacts, my reaction time will be even slower, as we discussed in Chapter 2. This means I would have to pick up the ball when it was around eight or nine yards away from me to have enough time for the correct eye-hand reaction.) The quarterback times when he throws the ball from the moment of snap to the time he thinks that I will see it to catch it, thus the reason this is called a timing pattern.

These plays are practiced over and over so that the ball is where the receiver expects it at the exact time. By practicing together enough, anticipation becomes a part of this equation and helps both athletes. Through repetition, the receiver can project where and when the ball will arrive. This may allow the receiver to start his eye-hand-body reaction process earlier. Both the receiver and the passer are on the same team; they can plan and practice ahead. In the example above, where I am the receiver, this would mean that I would not need the full six yards (or eight yards!) to see the ball but that I could just turn and expect the ball to be there.

Many athletes' reactive movements have been so trained by repetitive practice that some impulses don't have to make it to the decision-making part of the brain but can be handled more by reflex. When an athlete is in the trained reflexive response mode, the eye takes a picture, and on the way to the decision-making part of the brain, the impulses go through an area that says, "Been there, done that a million times." Conscious thought is avoided, and the learned response is made quicker than before. The brain may say, "This is what it is," but it doesn't have to go through the, "Here is what I need to do" step.

You can probably see now why intercepting a pass is tougher to accomplish. The interceptor is on the opposite team from the passer, so he has never practiced passing and receiving; the timing is solely up to the interceptor. The athlete has to see the ball at the exact time to react and get to the right place. How many times have you seen someone who should have had an interception just seem to lose the ball immediately as it hits his or her hands? Or try to field a line-drive softball or baseball too fast and drop it? Guess what? Those athletes probably saw the ball a moment after it had crossed the reaction-time threshold for them to get their bodies to the right spot. If you're watching when this happens, you'll notice that the athlete's body still completes the motions. It's just too late. The hands almost completed the task. They were almost there, but they weren't there at the exact time.

Getting back to the trained reflexive response mode, this is achieved only through many hours of repetitive practice. (You'll see me refer to this notion as "practice, practice, practice" throughout this book.) I'll give you two different ways to look at this point by using other authors' examples.

In his book *Outliers: The Story of Success*, the author Malcolm Gladwell discusses the "10,000 hour rule" in which experts feel that a minimum of 10,000 hours of practice are needed for a person's brain to bring together all the things that are required to become a true master of a craft or skill. He talks about people—like Bill Gates and the Beatles—who became huge success stories, which takes both talent and being in the right place at the right time. But he feels that one of the biggest factors that made them megasuccesses was that they completed their 10,000 hours of practice early in life as well as at the right time in terms of what was occurring in society. Ten thousand hours equates to around three hours of practice a day, or 20 hours a week, for 10 years.

Joan N. Vickers breaks down this thinking on vision to the smallest detail in her book, *Perception, Cognition, and Decision Training: The Quiet Eye in Action*. She talks about how athletes bank memory pictures in their brains of all the repetitive plays they have practiced. She feels that when athletes are performing a sports task, they rely on this memory bank so that they can go back into it and pull up the picture of the task they are trying to perform and then match it. She uses this reasoning to explain why many of the pictures of Arizona Cardinals All-Pro wide receiver Larry Fitzgerald Jr. show him with his eyes closed while he's making his catches. He's performed the task so many times that he doesn't need to rely on his eyes as much as on a mental picture from his memory bank to put his body in the proper position.

Ten thousand hours of practice gives athletes a lot of time to visually bank the many scenarios they undergo during their sport. This is enough practice time for athletes to know where to look, how to focus, how to move their bodies, and when to record the outcome for future reference.

> *See to Play Tip 10:*
> *Eye-hand-body coordination is enhanced throughout a lifetime by many hours of practice and repetition.*

Elite athletes live in the world of great eye-hand-body coordination. Elite athletes lacking in stature or speed compared to their peers usually make up for those deficiencies with better coordination and reaction skills. So the questions in my mind are:

- Is this a superior trait that elite athletes just have from birth?
- At what age do they have to begin to "use it" before they "lose it"?
- Is everyone equal in eye-hand coordination at birth, but the elite athletes just start using it earlier than everyone else?
- If it's a trait from birth, can you start training and exercising an athlete without the superior eye-hand coordination trait to overcome this deficiency and ultimately catch up to the

elite?

Because it seems to take a lot of practice to develop the eye-hand-body skills needed to become an elite athlete, I began wondering if all these athletes could just jam-pack all this practice into a few years or if it would be better to start at a young age. I decided to read up on great athletes to see how old they were when they started playing with a ball.

Joe Namath, quarterback great and NFL Hall of Fame member, had developed a good throwing arm and swing of the bat in the game of baseball by the age of six.

Joe Montana, quarterback great and NFL Hall of Fame member, has said that he pretty much had a ball in his hands by the time he left the crib. His father was the coach of several different sports and helped Joe develop some of his strongest traits as an athlete at a young age.

Michael Jordan, one of the NBA's all-time best players, started playing pitch-and-catch with his dad at around the age of five.

Hank Aaron's grandfather taught him a game of hitting bottle caps with a broomstick at an early age. Hank beat Babe Ruth's MLB home-run record and held it for 33 years.

Willie Mays started playing with a stick and ball around the age of one, about the same time he learned to walk. He is currently fourth on the all-time MLB home-run list.

Pete Rose, Major League Baseball's all-time hitting leader, started sports at a very young age. His father was determined to make him an athlete and even had him learn how to switch-hit in childhood.

Ted Williams, considered to be professional baseball's all-time best hitter, was shown a picture of an 18-month-old swinging a bat. He said that the child had a perfect swing. That child was Wade Boggs, one of baseball's best hitters, who is now in baseball's Hall of Fame.

Wayne Gretzky, considered the best NHL player of all time, was two when he started skating and six when he started playing organized hockey.

Mia Hamm had older, soccer-playing brothers and sisters, so she started playing soccer at a very young age.

Tennis Hall of Fame great John McEnroe started hitting a ball with a plastic bat at the age of two. His father reported he could hit it a great distance by the age of four.

The father of tennis great Andre Agassi hung a tennis ball over Andre's crib when he was an infant. When Andre was two, his father sawed most of the handle off of a tennis racket and had Andre start hitting a ball. By the age of four, Andre began to visualize playing against Jimmy Connors and switched to playing against tennis great Bjorn Borg at the age of nine.

Tiger Woods' father cut off the end of a golf club so that Tiger could start playing golf at around the age of one.

Australia's Don Bradman—the best cricket player of all time and, some argue, the best batsman in all of ball sports—began working on his eye-hand coordination after the age of two by spending hours hitting a golf ball off the curved brick base of a water tank and a tree stump.

I also started thinking about musicians. There is a lot of eye-hand coordination in playing music—seeing a note written on paper and translating that into coordinated finger movements. How young were the greats when they started? Beethoven was four years old. Mozart started playing piano at the age of five. Bach and Tchaikovsky were six years old.

In Chapter 1 I discussed how important it is to get children in to the eye doctor's office for their first eye exams by around the age of two because the visual system does a lot of fine-tuning between the ages of two and six. For the same reason, I believe it is important to begin work on eye-hand-body coordination early as well. This wiring of the visual system with the brain and body at an early age seems to have benefited those athletes who eventually made it to the ranks of the elite.

---

***See to Play Tip 11:***
***Most elite athletes started practicing their eye-hand-body***
***skills early in life, well before the age of six.***

---

The next questions I start thinking about are:

- When does repetitive practice lead to burnout?
- If burnout occurs, what steps can be taken to counteract it?
- What exercises outside of an athlete's particular sport can enhance his or her eye-hand-body coordination?

Coaches, trainers, and sports-vision doctors have worked hard as a community to develop all types of exercises outside the repetitions of athletes' normal sports motions that are intended to improve their eye-hand-body coordination. These can be used as homework for the athlete so that the athlete can continue working on improving eye-hand-body coordination without the worry of mental burnout or muscle injury through the repetitive nature of normal practices in a particular sport. The exercises that I use to help train athletes' eye-hand-body coordination can be broken down into two groups: *fixed-space eye exercises* and *free-space eye exercises*.

Fixed-space eye exercises are done with computers and machines that confine an athlete to a fixed place. Electronic devices allow the eye doctor to manipulate the exercise so that it is performed at exact times and in specified patterns. Reaction times can be measured, scored, and compared. Improvement can be documented.

Eye doctors use fixed-space machines to measure eye-hand-body coordination so that we can rank athletes and measure individual improvement. The machine I use in my ranking system is a board hanging on a wall that displays 100 points of light. The athlete stands in front of the board in an athletic position. The lights on the board start lighting one at a time in a random fashion. The goal is to have the athlete touch each light with his fingertip as it lights up. The changing pattern of the lights starts moving faster as the athlete hits the lights faster and more accurately. One program on the machine gives a score after the session that can be used to compare one athlete to another on this particular task. Other programs can be used as eye exercises for athletes to train the areas in which they have weaker tendencies in their eye-hand reaction time.

I do have an issue about using these machines to rank athletes. I think that to make the test reliable, every athlete in a group of athletes that is going to be ranked needs to be at an even starting place. This means that the test should be something that none of the athletes have seen before or something that they have all had an equal opportunity to practice. I think that this gives a more accurate comparison. I challenge others who are ranking or testing athletes to do the same, which again means either:

- Allowing the athletes to all have an equal amount of time practicing the eye-hand coordination test, or
- Performing a test that none of the athletes have seen before.

By following either of these two steps, the tester will get more reliable results. If these steps were not taken, an athlete with lesser talents who has practiced the test for an extended period of time will be more familiar with the test and can perform better than the elite athlete who has never done the test. Because the lesser athlete performed better mainly because of familiarity with the test, the results will give the tester a false sense of who is the better athlete.

Eye-hand-body exercises that are performed outside of computers or machines are known as free-space eye exercises. These are the exercises I prefer to recommend because athletes perform these exercises in an unconfined space. These exercises use familiar objects such as balls, strobe lights, and cards. Free-space exercises involve performing repetitive sports-type drills. These exercises take athletes out of their normal day of sports practice. There are even exercises that I recommend for athletes to use the morning of a game day to help them warm up and focus. Other exercises I recommend for the evenings of practice days, thus acting as homework to enhance and complement their skills. In Chapter 12 you will find the free-space-eye-exercise program that I recommend athletes use to get started with sports-vision training. My favorite exercises are the Ball Toss exercises, which can be combined with core training.

Many people ask me which type of training is better, free space or fixed space. I explain to people that the answer to that question is just like trying to find which diet works the best for someone wanting to lose weight. There are many diets and programs, but there is no one way that works best for all people. It's the same with this type of vision and body training. The exercises and programs that work the best depend on where the athlete's weaknesses lie.

As I stated earlier, I am more in favor of free-space exercises because free space is where the athletes are playing their sports. In other words, while playing their games, they're in the real world and not tethered to a computer. I think that basic exercises for improving eye-hand-body coordination are the best, so my favorites use a tennis ball and can be done anywhere. They develop eye-hand speed as well as give the athletes a chance to develop a soft touch with their fingertips. Getting athletes' bodies in motion during these exercises adds to the degree of difficulty and also adds an element of physical training. I won't go over all of these exercises in detail because they can be found later in the book. I will, however, mention some strategies. For exercises that require the use of a ball, I recommend dull old tennis balls because they are harder to see. A darker ball makes the task visually harder. The trainer can use physical contact with the athlete, known as *perturbation*, which causes interference during the exercise and requires greater concentration on the athlete's part. Increased difficulty can be reached by doing these exercises on a balance board.

These seemingly simple tennis-ball exercises are also some of the most multifaceted exercises an athlete can perform. As we've discussed in earlier chapters, eye focusing, eye movement, and eye-muscle strength can be trained by working with balls. These exercises help improve eye-hand-body coordination and trained reflexive responses. But as Pete Friesen will attest, they are also one of the best ways to actually improve the body's flexibility and mobility while strengthening areas where athletes aren't as fluid with their eye-hand-body responses. Pete has told me he loves watching how athletes begin to loosen up and get a fuller range of motion simply by responding to the desire to

catch the ball and that this type of workout is a fun way for the
athlete to get a better-working body. He also loves how they can
be used to strengthen the core. (As I've stated before, Pete has to
be the best trainer in the nation when it comes to marrying this
type of vision training with intense physical training. He feels
his athletes' responses to this type of training are phenomenal.)

I'd like to finish with a few more thoughts about eye-hand-
body coordination. Chapter 3 discussed athletes being in the
zone. It seems that athletes are talking about their eye-hand-
body coordination when they describe being in this athletic
state of nirvana. Here the mind and body are performing and
reacting in perfect harmony. Senses seem to be heightened. The
world around them seems to be moving in slow motion. The
puck/ball/hole seems to be larger than normal. They seem to
be using more reactive reflex power than brainpower. The brain
is acting like a passenger along for the ride and enjoying every
minute of it.

---

*See to Play Tip 12:*
*Good eye-hand coordination allows the world and*
*activity to move slower and objects to appear larger,*
*helping athletes reach the zone.*

---

The exact opposite occurs when athletes with great eye-
hand-body coordination start using their brains more and
start "thinking about it" too much. How many times have your
athletes performed at a lower level after overanalyzing the play?
Their thought process starts to interfere with their reaction
process. You will usually hear the coach shout, "Shake it off!"
or, "Quit thinking about it and just play!" This certainly helps
explain slumps, which are periods of time when an athlete just

can't seem to get things to go right because his or her brain is jumping in and actually interfering with eye-hand-body coordination. Through help with visualization and mental preparation found in Chapters 8 and 12, athletes can actually prepare for these times by developing tools to refocus their brains, to leave the thinking mode and get back into the playing mode.

Hopefully you've been able to tie the important parts of the past chapters together to understand how vital each aspect of the visual system is for the proper development of eye-hand-body coordination. Athletes have to see to play. If they can't see as clearly as they could, if they are under- or overcorrected in their prescription, if their eyes aren't pointed in the right direction, if their eye muscles don't work as a team and move smoothly, then each hour that they practice to improve their eye-hand-body coordination is a counterproductive hour. The timing that their body learns from an incorrect or imperfectly functioning visual system is not the exact timing that is needed to ultimately become an elite athlete. Again I'll point out that athletes need to get to an eye doctor at a very young age—and then be rechecked frequently throughout their lives to ensure that the work that they do to develop their eye-hand-body coordination is the most productive work that they can perform.

# CHAPTER 7
## VISUAL NOISE

Imagine you are a college basketball player. You are playing against your team's biggest rival in their gym, which is filled with 15,000 screaming fans. It's the championship game. The game is tied. There is a tenth of a second left to go in the game. You get fouled. You miss the first shot of a two-shot foul, so you only have one shot left. The other team calls a timeout, which has just now ended. You step up to the foul line, where the referee hands you the ball. The crowd is screaming. You bounce the ball and look to find the rim 15 feet away. The backboard is made of a transparent material so you see the hundreds of fans around it and behind it rooting against you, jumping up and down, and waving their big orange noodles. The backboard and rim appear to be floating and engulfed in this sea of bouncing humanity and orange noodles. You focus on the front of the rim and try to ignore the motion of all the waving stuff behind it.

Sounds pretty intense, huh?

Your brain is being bombarded by input from your eyes. The fans and their orange noodles are visual noise. You are accustomed to practicing in a gym, with no fans or movement in the background. The backboard and rim are easily visible. You have no problems concentrating on the rim in that atmosphere. Your brain is on cruise control there. Not so when your eyes start sending the brain input from things that you are not used to seeing. You have to learn to filter out those distractions.

Visual noise can affect the way that athletes perform, but not many athletes realize that the best way to combat it is to prepare for its presence. We know it exists. We know there are forces out there trying to break our concentration, creep into our heads and make us fall short in our athletic endeavors. The crowd screams loud. Whistles blow. Opposing players talk smack, as do fans, and things are going on all around that, if allowed to enter the thought process in a negative way, can distract the athlete.

Throughout this book, you've learned that if there is something wrong with athletes' visual systems, they will have a harder time reaching their genetic potential in their athletic performance—they can't see to play. Visual noise goes a step further. Visual noise is visual input that disrupts the brain's thought processes or trained reflexive responses enough to negatively influence the athlete's performance, so that the outcome becomes less than it could have been. In other words, athletes perceive something visually that makes them miss or change their movement or, at a minimum, makes it harder for them to concentrate. The visual noise is taking the brain out of playing mode and causing it to go into thinking mode.

First, let's look at the term *noise* to make it easier to understand. Most of us relate to the word *noise* by thinking of it as audio, something that we hear. My family's farm was built in the 1850s in a very rural area of West Virginia. I can remember going to visit my grandparents in the 1970s and sitting on the front porch. The first thing that struck me was how utterly quiet it was there. There was no television. There weren't any radio stations. If the wind wasn't blowing or a squirrel wasn't playing around, we wouldn't hear a thing. Especially after it snowed. Maybe we would hear our chairs creak. Maybe we would hear some muffled talk from inside the house. Maybe we would hear our heartbeats or our stomachs growl...but that was it! Total silence with no noise.

Now, if I'm sitting on my deck in Raleigh, North Carolina, in the summertime, it's a different story. First, I hear my air conditioner. I also hear the hum of air conditioners from my neighbors' houses. I hear cars as they go by the front of the house as well as the hum from traffic and engines in the distance. I hear birds chirping and squirrels rustling around. I hear kids playing outside. I hear dogs barking in the background. I hear my kids in the house having a big discussion; about, "Who touched my stuff?" I hear their music playing. I hear an airplane fly overhead. You get the picture. I hear a ton of stuff to which my attention may be diverted and that may alter my thinking process. The likelihood of hearing something that will really grab my attention—the loud bang of a car engine backfiring, car brakes screeching, or police sirens blaring—is much greater for me sitting on my deck at home than out in the fields of West Virginia.

So, if you are sitting with me reading this fine book in West Virginia, there are not a lot of sounds for you to ignore, and chances are there won't be any sounds loud enough to interrupt your train of thought as you read. If you're sitting with me on my deck here in Raleigh and reading, chances are good that you are going to hear a sound that will disrupt your train of thought and cause you to look up from this book. (Don't do it!) At minimum, you're going to have to ignore more sounds to concentrate on the task at hand.

Crowd noise at sporting events does a lot to get the adrenaline pumping for the athletes on the home team and may interfere with how the visiting team performs. The Carolina Hurricanes play at the RBC Center, which is considered one of the louder places to play in the NHL, and visiting teams report being bothered by the loud fans at times. College and professional football teams realize that crowd noise is a factor that affects team performance. As a result, many teams now incorporate loud noises during their practices. They blast loud music or recorded fan noise over the public-address systems to prepare the athletes for an upcoming game in a loud venue.

Visual noise can work in this same negative way. And the brain allows way more input from the eyes than from the ears, which makes visual noise much harder to ignore than audible noise.

Our brains take in a lot of information from our eyes. One of my summer jobs growing up was taking people on tours of a local cavern. I would point out the stalactites and stalagmites. One of my favorite things was to show people what total darkness was like. I would shut off the lights, and they could not see a thing. They couldn't even see their hands in front of their faces. They couldn't see the people beside them. They couldn't see their feet. They couldn't see the ceiling or the floor. If it weren't for gravity, I doubt they would have been able to tell which way was up. There were no cell phones to break the darkness. There were no digital cameras with the red or green lights on. It was just dark. Real dark! Totally dark!

Now, imagine that you are there with me in the cavern when we turn the lights back on. First, you notice that the lights seem brighter than before they were turned off. Then, you start getting the information that, *Oh yeah, I'm in a cave. I'm on a tour. There's the floor. There's the group ahead of me.* You start visually processing the world around you so that you can maneuver the rest of the way through the tour and take in the information you need to learn about the cave world.

As athletes visually take in the world, they look for their targets. They look for clues all around them. What's going on? Where are they? Where's the ball? They get information on space and speed. They get information about opposing players. Their brains get visual input so that they have the essential things needed to help them perform their tasks to their best abilities. Visual noise begins at a point where an athlete starts processing visual information that is not needed for his task, which can add confusion to the brain's decision-making process. Elite athletes are able to ignore the useless information that their vision is giving them and concentrate on the visual input that they do need.

I was talking with my daughter's high school trainer, Brent Dorenkamp, about visual noise. He gave me a great example to share here. He works with a company that promotes and coordinates triathlons. He said that in a recent triathlon, the company ordered swim caps printed with the event's name for the participants to have as a souvenir or keepsake after the race. The company decided they would like to brighten things up, so they picked the color orange for the caps—a bright, fun color that is easy for everyone to see when the athletes are in the water. Fast-forward to when the triathletes started the race: All 50 or more of them jumped into the water and headed for the turning point, a buoy out in the middle of the lake. The first swimmer made the turn around the buoy without any problem. So did the second and the third. But with the rest of the pack, the swimmers became confused and had to slow down. You see, the buoy was just about the same color as the swim caps, and it didn't rise up much higher out of the water than the swimmers' heads. These swimmers started having trouble distinguishing between the orange competitors' caps and the orange buoy that was their signal for the turn. Now, that's a lot of visual noise. The swimmers had to slow down to filter through the visual noise of all those random bobbing orange things to determine where the exact place to turn was. Their race was adversely affected by this visual noise.

That is an example of blatant visual noise, but visual noise can come in more subtle forms as well. If you play golf, visual tricks are used just about everywhere on the course to increase the difficulty of the game. Some fairways may look very narrow from the tee box, making golfers nervous about hitting a ball out of play, but after they hit the ball and walk to it, they find out that the area opens up a lot more than they thought. When they're ready to hit their approach shot onto the green, they have to figure out what the area around the pin is like. Bunkers and bushes might surround the green, giving the illusion that the green slopes one way, but it turns out to be the exact opposite. Another visual trick that golf-course designers use is to put false fronts near greens that seem to be the perfect place to hit the ball; meanwhile, the pin is actually further back, and the false front is too steep for the ball to stay on. These visual tricks— examples of visual noise—are incorporated into the design of a golf course to confuse golfers and affect their games in a negative manner.

Pete Friesen will tell you that he considers the advertising along the boards of hockey venues to be visual noise. Each arena is different. The boards along the edge of the ice are different as well, with some being darker than others. The darker boards further distract by making it more difficult to see the puck. Some arenas have light boards for advertising that go around the middle of the seating area; these can create strobe effects, adding to visual noise. Pete adds visual noise to the eye-hand-body exercises he uses on athletes to help them prepare for the visual noise present in play, and he feels this also helps the players increase their concentration levels.

Motion around us can create visual noise. Going back to my discussion of proprioception in the eye-hand-body coordination chapter, you may remember we talked about sitting in a parked car when another car backs out of the adjacent spot, causing your brain to get the sensation that your own body and car are moving forward. Your vision tricks your body into this feeling.

The dorsal visual stream, which is part of the proprioception system, really adds to motion sickness. For those of you who have been on a boat and have gotten motion sickness, you know what I am talking about. The inner ear houses the vestibular canals, which start feeling the motion. If you're down in a small cabin, your eyes see the cabin rocking up and down, the information is sent to the brain, and your visual system, in a sense, has just multiplied your motion sickness. For this reason, one of the main ways that people are taught to calm down motion sickness while on a boat is to go to the main deck of the ship and look at the horizon. The eyes see the line of the horizon, which is a reference of stability, and feed that information into the dorsal visual stream, which helps the brain offset the stimulus being sent from the inner ear.

Beginning figure skaters and dancers are given similar direction about how to use their eyes when they are learning how to spin. They are only allowed to do one or two spins at first. They are taught to visually catch the horizon or a spot in the room after each spin, which helps them not feel the motion of the spin as much. They use this input from the ventral, or conscious, visual stream to counteract the information the brain receives from the dorsal visual stream, the inner ear, and the other proprioceptors of the body. They are allowed to work up to more spins as they develop this technique for keeping straight their orientation within their surroundings.

In Chapter 3, we talked about triathletes who had trouble with others swimmers close to them while competing. The splashing of the water and movement from other athletes' arms cause visual noise that makes it hard for the swimmers to see the land markings that they use in their peripheral vision to let them know where they are on the course and how far along they are in the race.

The things we wear over our eyes can create noise. My contact lens dried up and moved around on me, creating visual noise when I played football. Athletes who wear contacts around water sports can get water in their eyes, causing the lenses to move around or pop out. (Take a contact lens-wearing crew member on a rowing team. Water splashed on her contact could potentially cause it to slip out.) An athlete who has a contact lens pop out has a tremendous amount of visual noise because the vision in one eye is blurry while the vision in the other eye is clear. Athletes should prepare for those moments by having backup contacts in the trainer's bag or the closest place to the playing field or competition venue.

My oldest daughter is a swimmer. On one of her 100-meter backstroke events in a 25-meter pool, she took the first flip turn. When she came back up to the surface, she had accidentally knocked her goggles to her nose, and water was splashing in her eyes. This caused one of her contacts to pop out, and she had to adjust how she got her visual cues to stay in the middle of the lane. She was able to stay in the middle of the lane, completed her remaining two turns, and finished the race in a decent fashion because this had happened to her once before in practice and she was mentally prepared. She also had a couple of extra contacts with her, so after she put a new one in her eye, she was ready to continue the day of competition.

If you think back to Chapter 2, we learned that athletes have the tendency to miss to the side of their better-seeing eye. This means that if a basketball player is wearing two contacts and the contact lens in his right eye pops out during a game, we would expect him to miss more shots to the left side of the rim or basket.

Sports glasses that we wear can get sweat on them and fog up. Sports glasses also only provide correction for a defined area in our field of vision, so the edge of the lens and the frame, as well as the decreased peripheral vision, can cause visual noise. Other forms of protective eyewear can get in the way of seeing, too. Hockey players who don't like to wear visors say visual noise is the main reason they don't wear the protection. They feel that the lower edge of the visor gets in the way of seeing the puck on the ice and that looking through the lens seems to distort their perception of the arena.

The sun and bright lighting can create visual noise also. The Cincinnati Reds play in Great American Ball Park, and hitters say that there are times when the sun reflects off of the windows of the stadium behind center field, making it hard to find the ball coming from the pitcher. In Chapter 2 Chris Richard talked about how the low lighting of the Richmond stadium made it hard for him to see the pitch in order to hit the ball, which shows that a decrease of visual cues is also a type of visual noise.

Not only can the bright reflection of the sun create visual noise that is then reflected off a window and into an athlete's eyes, but different colors in the light spectrum create more visual noise than others. You may have noticed that the sky is blue. This is because blue is the shortest wavelength in the visible light spectrum, and it bounces around the most. It is the color that you see the most on a hot, humid, hazy day. Blue creates the most visual noise. Put on an amber-tinted or pair of blue-blocking sunglasses and all of a the sudden you can see more clearly.

> **See to Play Tip 13:**
> **Elite athletes can filter visual noise and**
> **keep their concentration.**

The best way to beat visual noise is to practice how to deal with it and then to be prepared for it. In the golf example earlier, one could practice the course and memorize its traits, perhaps getting a caddy who knows the lay of the land so he can talk it through and let the player know what to expect. That's a pretty easy and straightforward way to train for visual noise.

But how do you train for the free throw with all the crazy people in the background? How do you train a goalie to follow the puck when all the athletes are moving in front of him and trying to screen him? How do you train a receiver to catch a football when someone is jumping in front of him or, even worse, the inevitable big hit is about to happen?

I train athletes to prepare for visual noise by actually adding visual noise to their vision exercises. This helps them improve their concentration levels and decreases the chance that this type of noise will sidetrack them. Many of the vision exercises that you find in Chapter 12 have variations that add visual noise as a component of the training routine.

An easy way for you to add visual noise to most exercises on your own requires that you to go to your local party store or electronics retailer and purchase a strobe light. Take the strobe light and a tennis ball to a dark room in your house and pick a wall that you can throw the ball against so that it bounces off and returns back to you. If you have someone else to work out with, you can play pitch-and-catch instead. Turn the strobe on so that it flashes quickly. (Do not do this if you suffer from seizures because strobe lights can trigger this problem.) Now, turn the lights off and play pitch-and-catch against the wall or with your partner. Once you get comfortable doing this with the strobe light flashing quickly, change the strobe to flash at a slower speed. You'll notice that you have to concentrate more as the strobe slows down. Continue to work on this so that the flash gets slower and slower. The slower the flash, the harder the visual task becomes because of the increased visual noise. You have to begin to project the path of the ball, and finding it becomes harder each time.

Nike has made strobe specs, the Vapor Strobe, which ath-letes can use to provide this strobe effect anywhere they train. (They are available at your eye doctor's office.) I think these are a great training tool because athletes are not limited to being in a dark room to utilize the strobe effect; they can be in their normal sports environment. These eyeglasses create a strobe effect that athletes have to concentrate through in order to make a catch, shoot a free throw, or perform a normal sports act that they are used to doing. It is important to mention here that athletes using the strobe effect should be training at a considerably slower speed than usual. The trainer must take care not to put athletes in situations that have the potential for injury. In other words, a receiver can wear these glasses and go out on a pass pattern, but this should not be done at full speed or against an opponent. Basketball players can use these glasses to practice free throws and shots, but they shouldn't be running down the court at full speed with them on.

In my office I have other gadgets that add visual noise. For example, I have a technique that combines exercises with *yoked prisms*. These are special lenses that shift the world considerably to the left or right. The glasses are easy to slip on and off and come with a string that goes around athletes' necks so that the player can quickly take the glasses off without dropping them. The receiver wears the lenses and catches the ball for several minutes with the world displaced by the glasses. (The ball actually looks like it's coming at them from five feet to the left or right of where it is actually.) Then the receiver takes the glasses off and catches the ball normally again for several minutes. We go back and forth with this several times. These exercises force athletes to adapt and concentrate.

These are just a few ideas on how to create visual noise to help train athletes to expect noise and improve concentration. It is easy to be creative and come up with your own types of visual noise out in the field. The point of this discussion is to validate that visual noise is present, like audible noise. We also have to realize that since vision supplies more information to the brain than the ears do, we need to put a larger emphasis on supplementing the athletes' workout and practices by incorporating visual noise. By trying to break their concentration and affect their game during practice, we ultimately will increase their concentration levels for game day.

In the last chapter, we talked about Larry Fitzgerald Jr., a wide receiver for the Arizona Cardinals. He was asked if there were any exercises that helped him become a premier receiver. He explained that his grandfather was an eye doctor in Chicago and that he started doing eye exercises at around the age of eight. These exercises helped him learn to use his eyes better, concentrate more, and they helped with his learning in the classroom.

He took these exercises home with him and also made up exercises of his own. One exercise that he liked to do entailed lying in bed at night with his lights off, throwing a football up in the air, and catching it in the dark room. He started doing this to help him get a feel for the ball. Catching a ball in the dark like that is the ultimate in visual noise because vision is interrupted almost completely. Some athletes use this sightless form of training by trying to practice a task while blindfolded.

I would also like to add a technique here that I teach to athletes that uses visual noise to break up their thought processes on purpose. It is meant to be used at times when they realize that they are stuck in a negative thought pattern, such as when they are in an anger mode, in a slump, or feel themselves obsessing about something they shouldn't be during a game. This technique helps distract the thinking brain to get it out of its negative spiral. I tell them to look across the room at a wall about 20 feet away and find two different spots on the wall that are separated by a distance of at least 10 feet. They are to look at the spot on the left, then look at the spot on the right, back to the spot on the left, and continue this back and forth as fast as they can. It is virtually impossible to continue thinking about what's bothering you after about 5 to 10 seconds of this motion. The visual information bogs down the brain. As a matter of fact, it's hard to get a conscious thought going when you're doing this. The key to making this technique successful in sports is to not go back to the negative subject that caused the problem in the first place and to use the visualization techniques found in the next chapter to direct the brain toward the right train of thought.

In this chapter, you've learned that not everything we see is a good thing in athletic performance. You know that athletes need to see to play, but you also learned that they have to ignore the noise that visually interferes with play. Some of what we see can be disruptive and can negatively affect athletic performance. The best way to prepare for this is by performing vision exercises that use visual noise to train us to concentrate better.

The next chapter is going to teach you how to use your mind's eye to help you mentally prepare for visual noise by moving your brain from playing mode into thinking mode.

# CHAPTER 8
## USING AND EXPANDING YOUR MIND'S EYE

We started the last chapter on the foul line, getting ready to take a shot in front of 15,000 screaming fans. Did you make the shot and win the championship game? Of course you did! You'd been mentally preparing for that moment your whole career. You had played the scenario over in your mind several times, especially in the days before the big game. You saw the foul shot sink into the basket amid the sea of orange noodles and humanity before the game ever took place. So your body and mind were prepared for the situation. The first foul shot—which you missed—was also part of a scenario that you had practiced before in your mind, so you were not mentally devastated by it and could move on easily to the most important moment: the shot you are getting ready to take right now. You mentally played the game before it happened, you are ready for the situation, and you can direct your play toward a successful outcome.

In Chapter 6 I talked about training the body's responses until a sports action doesn't require conscious thought, to get past "thinking mode" to "playing mode." You develop those trained reflexive responses from your past experiences. In this chapter, I'm going to describe how athletes can take their preparation a step further by using mental pictures to train the brain about outcomes that they can expect to encounter in future experiences. Using the mind's eye to create these mental pictures can help athletes develop a higher level of concentration and give their bodies the benefit of the lower level of stress that results.

What do I mean by the mind's eye? Most definitions that you will find state that it's the ability to see with the mind. I believe elite athletes expand this inner vision by incorporating other senses: what they're hearing, how their body feels, how they are breathing and what their heart rate is, even what they smell. So, to me the mind's eye is a place that not only houses images that we can draw on to prepare for future events, it also stores memories of physical states that we can use to project what our bodies will sense in those future scenarios. Athletes can prepare their minds for what they are going to see during future experiences, and they can also prepare for what their bodies are going to feel. This mental preparation allows athletes to avoid conscious thought while playing because the mind and body have already been there.

In June 2002 the Carolina Hurricanes made it to their first Stanley Cup Finals (including the franchise's past as the Hartford Whalers). They were playing against the Detroit Red Wings. The first two games of the best-of-seven series were played in Detroit in the famed Joe Louis Arena (talk about a sports arena with a history; if those walls could talk!). Hours before the drop of the puck in the first game, I caught a ride with a couple of the Hurricanes players from the hotel to the arena. We arrived and went to the dressing room.

On my way in through the arena seats, I noticed Rod Brind'Amour sitting near our bench, staring at the playing surface. He had arrived quite a while before us, I was told, and I noticed that he returned back to the locker room a long time after I had been in there.

The following season, I asked him about what he was doing out there in his solitude before the game. He explained to me that he was playing the game in his mind. I continued to quiz him on the details of what he was doing mentally and the techniques he was using with his mind's eye.

Shortly after Wade Boggs retired from playing baseball, he became a hitting coach for the Tampa Bay Rays. One afternoon I was in the locker room in Durham examining a few of the AAA boys when he was in town. I had a chance to talk with him for a while about how he used his mind's eye to prepare for games and also about how he was coaching his players to mentally prepare in a similar fashion.

As I mentioned in Chapter 3, NFL great Torry Holt explained to me in detail how he uses visualization to mentally prepare for games. He watches different game films to learn about the team that he is getting ready to play, and when he watches, he visualizes what is occurring on the field from several different perspectives. He puts himself in the place of the receiver going out on the pass route and imagines what he sees in his opponents. He also watches himself, the receiver, from the defensemen's eyes to get an idea of what they are seeing as they try to stop him, which he uses as a tool to consider different ways to mislead them or perfect his route. Finally, he watches the film to see the play unfold from the coach's eyes, giving him insights into why the play was called (that is, what the coach saw about the opponent that made running that particular play the best strategy).

Those three interviews, and interviews with hundreds of other athletes, have aided me in developing the way I help athletes use mental preparation. In this chapter, I will explain the mind's eye and break down how it can be used to help athletic performance. This information will give you a foundation to help athletes build a mental-preparation program of their own. You have learned how to see to play; now we're going to learn how to see to play into the future.

The elite athletes I have interviewed have told me how they use the mind's eye, through the use of visualization, to help them improve as athletes. Torry and a few of the other athletes I talked with use visualization the most, incorporating it into the hours they spend watching game films as well as preparing mentally for practice and games. Most athletes tell me that they use visualization to a lesser extent, which seems to translate to an hour or so the night before a game and then one or more shorter sessions as part of their game-day preparations. This was the routine that Wade told me he used the majority of the time. Some athletes include a session before leaving home or the hotel on game day. They may arrive early to the playing field and sit in the stands, as Rod did before that Stanley Cup game, and use the actual venue for the competition as a backdrop for their mental movies. Other players use their mental movie theaters while just sitting at their lockers, as part of their pregame mental preparations.

Other elite athletes report that they use visualization more minimally. They may use it only when they need to map out a picture of a new play or movement they are learning. Visualization helps them perform that task better, until their bodies have learned the task and they have developed more reflexive responses. These athletes don't use this as a tool for pregame preparations but turn to it when they are starting to falter with a certain play to help them see the correction they need to make.

---

**See to Play Tip 14:**
*Elite athletes use the mind's eye to help them achieve athletic goals and sports-specific tasks.*

Many athletes tell me that spending time tuned in to the mind's eye makes them feel calmer and more focused during a game as well. Their brains use mental pictures to rehearse the possible events of the game, helping them feel more relaxed and prepared. Visualization can be especially helpful when it is used to rehearse several possible scenarios. They feel they have a better grasp on the options to try next if they don't succeed at first. This keeps their mental and physical stress levels lower while they move on to another option for success.

To make sure we're all starting at the same point in this discussion about the mind's eye, I'll move along a logical path to the ultimate goal of improving athletic performance through stress management and concentration. Some athletes cannot make mental pictures, so I will start with a few easy ways to make a mental picture. One thing to note here: the mental pictures that I am talking about here are not the same as the ones that athletes have banked in their memories, which are used during play to initiate the trained reflexive responses discussed in Chapter 6. The pictures we are trying to make now are mental pictures of things that have not happened yet.

The next step in this picture-making process is to learn to turn your mental pictures into motion pictures. Once we learn how to do this, we can tackle the subject of using visualization to prepare for athletic performance.

For those who have not developed the art of making mental pictures, an exercise for developing this skill involves standing in front of a piece of artwork. I'll walk you through it so that you can try it yourself. Look all around the picture for a short period of time, then close your eyes and try to remember the details of the picture. Try to piece together the details of the picture like you would put together a jigsaw puzzle. Finally, open your eyes and compare your mental picture with the actual artwork. Ask yourself, "Are the colors the same?" "Are the objects in the correct spots?" and "What details are missing?"

When you're ready to make it more difficult, look at the picture again, then close your eyes and bring the picture back up in your mind's eye. After you have the picture in your mind, turn it over 180 degrees so that it is now completely upside down. What does it look like? Can you see the larger objects in the picture pointing upside down? Can you see smaller details upside down? Can you see the colors? Can you scan from left to right and see the relationships of the objects to each other in their new orientation? This technique really helps athletes train the mind's eye, especially if they couldn't do it before.

Let's move on to making motion pictures in your mind's eye. The easiest way to do this is by thinking about something pleasant that happened to you in the past. Do you have a favorite childhood memory? A moment in time that is easy to pull up in your memory bank?

The memory that I can go back to was the Christmas of 1975 when I got my new 10-speed bicycle from Santa Claus. I really wanted that bike, and I got it! I can still see the shape of the bike and its blue paint with white highlights. I can see the tires, the pedals, and the gears. I can still see the handlebars with the brake and clutch. I can still see the two gearshifts. I can still see the seat. I remember it was a snowy day in Indiana, with at least three inches of snow still in our driveway. I remember I didn't care about the conditions outside; I still had to go out and ride my new bike! I can feel the cold hitting my face as I went out the door. I can remember shivering because I still had on pajamas and no coat. I didn't care! It was awesome! I can still feel the energy that I had to exert because the snow created a terrible weight and drag. I can still feel how tired and drained I got from riding my new bike. What a great day! What a great memory!

Going back to this memory, I seem to have a little movie projector in my mind. I can see the picture. I can see the movement. I can also begin to add other senses because I remember sounds and smells as well as sights. This is a place in my mind where mental pictures are made from what my eyes have seen and my body has experienced, how I felt, and my physical surroundings. I can go to this place any time I want to by pulling out its recorded memory, like I would an old home movie. This is the mind's eye: a place in my brain that has combined a mental movie of that moment with the recordings made by my body and senses.

Now you try it. Find an old memory that's one of your favorites and bring it back. As you bring this memory back, think about not only the sights but the sounds and smells. Try to remember the feeling you had of excitement or joy. Try to bring that feeling back as you're running your moving picture of what was occurring. Also, think about your breathing and your heart rate. As we go into our mind's eye discussion, being able to control your body and the stress you feel is important, and this brief exercise allows you to begin to bring your body into the process.

Just as the mind's eye can help us relive the memories that are stored there, it can also make movies of events that haven't happened yet. This is the part of the mind's eye that we can use to help us improve athletic performance. We can make a movie of how we expect to play, how our opponents are going to react, and how our body is going to feel from the energy exerted as well as from adrenaline. We can even predict sounds and smells. Using the mind's eye like this to prepare for a future event is known as visualization. Visualization is the first step in preparing the brain to decrease stress and improve concentration.

I believe that there are four main tools that athletes can use to improve athletic performance:

- Visualization: The brain trains for the future.
- Relaxation: The brain finds a place of calm.
- Stress Management: The brain redirects itself to calm when stress tries to interfere.
- Concentration: The calm brain and body stay focused on the task.

We'll go over each of these tools in detail to show you how they can be incorporated into an athlete's game as well as the importance of these skills to elite athletes. I'm going to include some exercises in this chapter to help you use your own mind's eye. I also provide exercises in Chapter 12 to remind you to include these techniques in your athletes' training.

**Visualization**

Visualization is the process of making a mental motion picture of an event that hasn't happened yet. Athletes use this tool to make mental movies of how they are going to perform under certain circumstances so that they can plan for an upcoming athletic performance. This allows them to be mentally prepared for every aspect of a game. They can change the players they may be facing, they can picture the crowd, they can picture the environment, and they can run through alternate situations so that they're prepared to turn the outcome to their favor.

Let's get started visualizing!

You need to be in a quiet place where you won't be disturbed.

You need to be rested and not hungry, comfortably dressed, and relaxed and calm so that you can focus on your mind's eye. Most people do this with their eyes closed. Some do this with their eyes open but use a neutral or soft focus on a blank wall, the floor, or maybe at the playing field or surface as a backdrop.

Wade and Rod agreed that there are two perspectives that you should use when you make a mental movie:

1. The view from your eyes; your eyes are the camera that is making this part of the movie.
2. The view of you seen from the eyes of others; the camera or cameras making this part of the movie give you the views of a spectator in the stands, an opposing player, or a teammate. There are several possible views from this standpoint, and you need to choose the view that will help you the most as you prepare for a particular play.

Now make your movie.

1. The first movie is from your eyes. The first time through, pay attention to how the play goes in the best outcome. You see how everything around you appears. Start from a wide-angle view of the entire field or playing space and work your way in to a smaller, more detailed view. See all of the athletes around you then slowly converge on the opponent who is in front of you as you bring the play to success. Pay attention to where opponents come into view from outside and where your teammates are rallying around you for support.
2. Now rerun the play to visualize other realistic outcomes. Don't view these other possible outcomes as being negative but as experiences that you can use to your benefit by

readying your reaction skills. Use this step to prepare your mind for a time when you are not as successful as you were in your first visualization choice. See yourself miss the foul shot, but also visualize how you don't let yourself get disappointed so that you can go on to sink the second one, just like at the beginning of this chapter.

3. See yourself playing with your current skill level. Don't fantasize and do something that is not humanly possible. Stay within your limits. Fantasy is an enemy in this drill. (However, you can prepare for how things may go if you were playing slightly above your skill level, just in case things go better than expected.)

4. Feel how your body feels and what you are experiencing physically. Feel your breathing. Feel your heart rate. This helps prepare your body.

5. Be aware of sounds and what is going on around you. Include the waving orange noodles we talked about in the last chapter or any other distractions or visual noise that could be present.

6. Play all of these movies again from the eyes of a spectator.

7. Play all of these movies again from the eyes of a coach to get a better understanding of why the play was called.

All athletes have ebbs and flows with their performances. Using visualization, athletes can prepare for different outcomes without letting them turn into the beginnings of a slump. When athletes prepare by thinking through all of the possibilities and not just the one they most want to take place, they will be more successful at steering themselves out of the doldrums before they have a chance to get stuck.

Another way that you can use visualization to get through

a period of lower performance is to replay times when you were more successful. You are the successful athlete. Remember how you felt, how things moved slower, how your body felt, etc. You are getting ready to get back to that time of success and have already started down that path. You can tell yourself, "Oh yeah, I remember there was a time I didn't do well, but I remember I started doing much better, and this is how I did it, by being myself, and now I feel the stress fading away." You can sense and feel that your mind and body are ready to tear it up!

Rod emphasized to me how important it is to end your visualization on a positive note but not with a fantasy. An example of a fantasy in hockey would be if, in your mind's eye, you always scored after every shot. A more realistic—and better—approach to visualization is one where you visualize your shot but make a picture of the puck bouncing off the goalie pads, your reaction of getting the rebound, and your score from hitting the rebound back into the goal. Other times, visualize your shot just missing to the side of the goal and then bouncing off the boards back to you as you rush in for the rebound. Visualize different plays and every possible scenario of where you will be at different times on the ice. Visualize the goalies you will face and their tendencies. (Wade told me he would spend time in the evenings before games visualizing the pitcher he was facing the next day and replaying the different tendencies and arm motions that pitcher had.)

In some sports, winning is the only option to visualize. I talked about this with Mary Whipple, who is currently in training for the 2012 Olympics in London. She told me that visualization is an important part of her team's training. When they travel to various races, their practice days leading up to the event end by meeting in a room where all nine members of the crew can find a place to sit or lie comfortably. The lights are turned off and they close their eyes as Mary goes over their race plan. She then goes on to describe events before the start of the race in detail: where they are located, how they feel, the weather, the wind, the water, the crowd, and the surroundings. The team listens as she takes the place of the announcer and presents the teams. Then she instructs her team to get ready as she barks out the start. Each of her crewmates visualizes what she sees during the race. They visualize the person in front or behind them and their craft. They visualize their oars as they see themselves compete. They listen to Mary as she yells out directions to keep them in unison and performing at peak level. They feel their bodies and know what to expect as Mary describes how their craft is faring as it reaches each important marker in the race. Mary and her team continue this visualization exercise for the full six minutes that it takes to complete the race. Mary describes in detail how close the race is, right up to the finish. The teammates can feel the intensity. Mary ends the race with a win. The teammates join in that feeling and can visualize the moment.

Another interesting story that Mary told me about using her mind's eye involves a technique that she uses at times to help improve the team's performance. She explained that there are instances during a race when she feels the team's output is not optimal, and she will actually close her eyes to get a better sense of what needs to take place to correct this. With her eyes closed, she feels the motion of the boat and the force of the rowers and tries to identify what is causing the team to underperform. This is a prime example of an athlete getting rid of visual noise, as we discussed in the last chapter, to allow her body (in particular her inner ear and proprioceptors) to give her mind's eye a picture of what is going on around her so that she can determine what is missing. She then opens her eyes and directs her team to make the change that needs to occur.

**Relaxation**

The best way to understand the process of relaxation is to think of your brain or state of consciousness as a multilayered entity such as an onion. An onion has an outer layer of skin. Peel that off, and you find another layer that looks and feels different from the outside. Opening the onion even more, you find another layer even more different from the first two. You can continue to do this until you reach the center, which is small, round, and tough to break.

Your mind or psyche functions at many different levels. I've heard this explained many times using this same metaphor of an onion. The outside level operates more on the activities that you go through on a day-to-day basis. As you peel off that layer and look further, you find your emotions in a deeper layer. Your feelings of good, bad, happy, and sad can bump up and interfere with your top layer of day-to-day activities. Going even deeper into this "mind onion" is the layer of your intense emotions, such as anger and hurt. Because this layer is smaller, rounder, and more compact, these feelings—when activated—can really start to build as they circle around their layer, building in intensity and ultimately disrupting all the layers that are above them. The anger and hurt cycle is a hard one to break. Below all these layers is the small center that is the basis of the mind: calm.

Relaxation is simply peeling back and turning off all these other layers of our minds to get to that center of calm. Athletes who find that area need to practice being in it and staying in it. Calm is the area where athletes want their minds to be while playing. Emotions, anger, and distracting thoughts are easier to keep in check when an athlete is calm. Concentration is easier to obtain and maintain in a state of calm.

There are many different relaxation techniques. It's important for each athlete to try several to determine which one works the best for him or her. Yoga and meditation are popular forms.

Here is a technique I use that combines visual imagery and communication with your body. Several athletes have told me that they use this type of technique. You should do this in a quiet place, as you did while learning your visualization technique, wearing similar clothing, not being tired or hungry. Sit in a chair or lie down on your back and stay perfectly still. Close your eyes. Imagine that you are by yourself at the beach on a warm and beautiful day. Feel the heat from the sun as it shines down on you. Feel the warmth as it moves over you. Hear the sound of the waves. Hear them as they rush in and then rush out. Feel yourself floating on a raft on those waves. Enjoy the relaxing motion of the waves. Let your body and muscles get real loose and relaxed.

Take a deep breath in and hold it for the count of five. Now, release it and feel the toxins in your body start to leave. Take another breath and do the same. Do this several times and feel your heartbeat as it relaxes; and you will feel your heart rate decreasing. Allow your mind to think about only your breathing and your heart rate as you hear and feel the ocean waves in the background. Continue deep, slow breathing as the toxins in your body leave.

Start to feel a wave of relaxation go over your body. You are heading to a place of calm. Feel the wave of relaxation as it hits your right big toe. You can feel how the wave comes and goes over your toe. You can feel a tingling and warmth in your toe. Now, the wave of relaxation slowly moves up to the arch of your foot. Feel it as it relaxes your ankle. You can feel it as it continues to move, and it slowly crawls up the calf of your leg. You can actually feel the calf muscle relax. Now it's over your thigh and you can feel it as those muscles relax. You can feel the tingle as the wave moves to the back part of your leg and slowly moves up to your lower back. You can feel the tingle as every muscle relaxes. Now the wave of relaxation is at your right shoulder. You can feel the shoulders as they loosen and relax. Feel your neck as it slowly starts to release that tension. Let it relax and loosen. Now the back of your neck feels the tingle of relief. Allow this tingle to continue for a while. Many of us hold a majority of our stress in our neck muscles, so this area needs more time to relax. Now, feel the tingle move down the muscles of your right arm, from your biceps and triceps down to your forearm and then into each individual finger. Then you feel the tingle as it crawls back up and across your neck to your left shoulder and then down your left arm. Now you feel it crawl up your arm and back out to your chest. You feel it move slowly over your body as it goes to the upper left leg. You feel it move around to the back of your leg, down to your calf, down to your ankle, down to your toe. Now it leaves, and you are totally relaxed and in a place of calm.

This state of relaxation is very important for your mind and your body. It gives your mind a break from its day-to-day overload—a chance to release, cleanse, and reboot. The mind also gets to reconnect with your body as it becomes in tune with your muscles, lungs, and heart. The body enjoys this state because as your heart rate decreases, your heart doesn't have to work as hard. Your blood pressure is lowered. The tension held in your muscles is relieved and the blood flow to your muscles is improved. Stress has been removed.

Like a bookmark used to mark the place in a book, athletes

like to remember this place of calm in their minds so they can return to it. Many use imagery, a picture in the mind's eye to relive or bring back a particular moment of calm, like:

- A time he was in the zone–the state of athletic nirvana–and everything was clicking. He remembers how everything was moving in slow motion, how his breathing felt, how fast his heart was beating.
- A childhood memory when she was totally relaxed and confident, like an old high school locker room, childhood room, or treehouse.
- A place he used to relax, like on a beach, at a park, or under a tree.
- A place she currently relaxes and meditates.

Regardless of the picture, it's a place the athlete can race to in the stress of game situations to help decrease stress and reinforce calm. Some players actually watch the crowd around them in order to get to a place of calm. Here are a couple of examples:

- Looking at a family in the crowd and observing what they are doing
- Looking at a waiter or salesperson in the crowd and watching the transaction

**Stress Management**

Now that you have used visualization to prepare your mind and body for what to expect during competition and have used relaxation techniques to find your area of calm, stress management is the tool you use to keep your mind and body in that state during competition. No matter how prepared you are and how quickly you can relax, there are going to be times when you feel stress. But you can prepare yourself so that during times of stress you will be able to refocus your brain back to that place of calm and toward an outcome that you have visualized. Managing stress is important for situations when your brain is getting sidetracked by thoughts that can negatively affect your game.

Here are a few of the methods that athletes have shared with me that they use to refocus their brains in stressful situations. They use them so that they don't focus on a negative but instead can clear their minds and start to focus more on a positive:

- Stepping back from the batter's box and counting the lines in the wood of the bat
- Counting the lines of tape on a hockey stick or evaluating the state of the tape
- Tossing a puck a certain number of times while concentrating on its print
- Retying a shoe or skate
- Performing the same physical routine before a given task, such as always preparing the same way for every pitch in the batter's box, or bouncing the ball at the free throw line the same way every time

These are all examples of putting the body through a strict routine so that the brain can disengage from a source of stress and go back to the place of calm. Once they have broken the stress cycle, athletes can go into a calmer mode. Some people view these routines as superstitions, but they are really just ways that athletes have developed to stay in that place of calm. Think of the drive home that you don't remember because you were daydreaming and your body was on autopilot. The athletes going through these routines are trying to get their bodies on autopilot so they can stay relaxed, focused, and get the brain back to playing mode and not thinking mode.

Athletes choose a technique for breaking up stress and do it the same way in every game and for every stressful situation. The method is not randomly chosen to get out of this situation or that but is always the same so that even getting out of stressful situations becomes routine for the athlete. There is nothing new. The athlete is merely doing things that he has done forever, and consistently, in his games. His stress-management technique breaks up his mind's deviation down the road toward stress and steers it back to the positive thinking that has to take place in order for him to be successful in his performance.

When the mind has changed its focus from a negative path and has moved to a calm zone or even gone a step further by moving onto a positive path, the next skill step for the athlete to master is how to concentrate on playing.

**Concentration**

Through the years, I've asked athletes how they concentrate or keep their minds in the game when playing. Wade Boggs told me he learned that "Concentration is the art of thinking about nothing." I don't know where he got those words, but they have definitely stuck with me.

I heard another former professional baseball player who was being interviewed on a sports show say something similar. He was asked to think back to his rookie year and remember what advice he was given from the veterans on the team that stuck with him through his career. He said that was easy. The advice that he leaned on the most was, "They told me to quit thinking and just react!"

Concentration is the art that athletes use to keep their brains in the game, and that allows their bodies to play to their genetic potentials without conscious thought shifting them away from that task. Extraneous thoughts become the enemy.

I hope this chapter has illustrated how important it can be for athletes to learn to use the mind's eye as part of their game-day preparations so that their brains can concentrate on playing, and to keep their brains in playing mode before, during, and after the game. Making mental pictures is the baby step to get athletes to learn to use visualization, which leads to relaxation, then to stress management, and finally to concentration. Their brains and bodies are relaxed. They use the mind's eye to see to play.

Visual noise, pain or physical contact, negative thoughts—all of these things can interfere with an athlete's ability to concentrate. Anything that takes an athlete's mind off of playing has a negative impact on performance. As we discussed earlier, usually the more we think in sports, the tougher it is to achieve our goals.

Concentration is really about getting to that happy place of calm and relaxation and staying there and staying focused, to keep the mind in playing mode instead of thinking mode. Realizing that it is human nature to wander off topic is the best defense to prepare an athlete for when lapses happen; implementing a stress-management routine is the best defense when they occur and can quickly get an athlete's mind back to the right spot again.

Using the mind's eye seems to be another trait that elite athletes use to give them an edge over other athletes. The extent to which they use this skill varies, but they all seem to have the ability to use techniques from all four of the tools discussed in this chapter.

As you can see, the mind's eye can be a powerful thing! I'd like to challenge you to use your mind's eye in your everyday life as well. The mind's eye can really improve the way you look at your life, today and in the future. The techniques in this chapter can help you become the person you want to be, improve your outlook on life, help you stay in that place of calm, and improve your ability to concentrate on the things that matter.

# CHAPTER 9
## LIFESTYLE CHOICES FOR ATHLETIC EYES

"Garbage in, garbage out" is a phrase that was created in the computer-science world to emphasize to beginning programmers the importance of being exact. Incorrect information being put into the computer causes incorrect results to come out.

This statement couldn't be truer for highly physically trained athletes. Take your average greasy cheeseburger and fries; most of us are pretty much in heaven. But it's important to consider how that greasy meal causes athletes to feel. I've heard countless stories of athletes talking about a short-term deviation from their normal healthy diets for a quick binge into Americana only to end up paying for it by physically getting sick. They literally feel the meal, or garbage, as it's going through their system, causing indigestion and an overall run-down feeling.

Proper rest is also an important factor to the success of these athletes' on-field performances. Their daily routines follow a strict regimen that includes getting the right amount of sleep and rest for their muscles. They just can't function as well in their sport if they haven't allowed their bodies to recover from the strain of athletics or fagitue.

I've noticed that these same lifestyle choices can also affect vision in the elite athletes I've tested. I've found that there are days when some of my 20/8 or 20/10 athletes don't test to that same high level. This suggests to me that factors such as nutrition and fatigue probably play a role in their varying acuity.

And if the eyes truly are the windows to the soul and are being negatively affected for these reasons, imagine what is happening to the body as a whole.

Other day-to-day choices that athletes make can also affect their vision and overall health in both the short and longer term, including the eye protection they choose and the people they call on when problems arise. For that reason, I decided to include a lifestyle section in this book to talk about the lifestyle changes that athletes can make to help keep their vision at an optimum level, which will ultimately help them physically.

> *See to Play Tip 15:*
> *Proper training, rest, and nutrition affect*
> *athletic performance and vision.*

**Nutrition**

I recently met Jennifer Ketterly, MS, RD, CSSD, at a seminar where we were both lecturers. She is the director of sports nutrition at the University of North Carolina and oversees the nutritional needs of the athletes in the university's varsity sports program. Because I have personally witnessed the role that nutrition plays in professional athletes' lives, have seen that philosophy in action at the collegiate level, and know that it is trickling down to the dining-room tables of the high school athlete, I asked Jen to contribute to this book by giving us some more insight into the world of sports nutrition and her thoughts on nutrition as it relates to vision. Here is what she wrote:

### *SPORTS NUTRITION: The Athlete's Last Legal Edge*

*When accuracy, endurance, and last seconds count, elite athletes must fine-tune all aspects of their performance in order to come out on top. In today's competitive environment, nutrition is an athlete's last legal edge. It's what I like to call one of the three "pillars of performance." Athletes who want to excel in their sport must become educated in all three areas: training, rest, and nutrition. Incorporating today's well-researched sports-nutrition principles can mean the difference between winning and losing, first or second place.*

*In addition to being one of the pillars that supports an athlete's performance by helping improve speed, strength, stamina, and training adaptations, sports-nutrition principles also prevent injury and promote health. For example at UNC we aim to prevent sports-related issues resulting from fatigue that leave an athlete at higher risks for injury and poor performance. We also closely address an athlete's nutritional needs before and after a major surgery to help ensure a smooth recovery and aid in the rehabilitation process. When an athlete is dealing with an injury, it is a great time to focus on nutrition.*

*Being properly fueled with adequate and appropriate nutrients prevents both mental and physical fatigue as well as builds and recovers lean body mass and energy stores. Nutrition also hydrates and helps identify and achieve optimal body weight and composition ranges. Showing up to practices and competitions properly fueled and well hydrated can ensure peak performance.*

*Young athletes in today's sports do not often recognize all three performance pillars and do a great job with their sport-specific training but may limit their capabilities by not incorporating rest, recovery, and nutrition into their regimens. Many college athletic departments employ registered dietitians to teach nutrition to their athletes and implement nutrition programs to help these athletes get the most out of their training and performance. At UNC, we have two full-time staff [members] to service our 28 varsity teams.*

*We offer individual counseling, team education sessions, and work with food-service providers to help coordinate meals and snacks that meet NCAA rules and the athletes' nutrition needs. In addition to those key functions, we also evaluate the use of nutritional supplements, design pre- and post-workout and game-day fueling strategies, and participate in preparticipation screenings to identify nutrition-related health and performance priorities.*

*Most professional ranks also incorporate nutrition expertise and can be found on the sidelines and in training camps working alongside other key support personnel. In addition to college and professional athletes, many active recreational athletes employ the principles of nutrition to get the most out of their training. Many state high school athletic associations are also beginning to recognize the importance of [educating athletes about] nutritional supplement use and potential abuse and [preventing] dehydration and heat-related illness. The sooner aspiring elite athletes can learn and implement these concepts, the further ahead their development can potentially be as compared to that of their peers or competitors.*

*Sports nutrition's influence can be seen in and around all of an athlete's environments. The athletic training room, weight room, practice fields, and locker rooms are all common fueling and recovery hot spots. For example, in many of our weight rooms at UNC, we have set up what we call "fueling and recovery stations" where athletes can go pre- or post-workout to choose an appropriate snack to help fuel the workout or begin the rebuilding and recovery process afterward. Nutrition can be seen in fitness clubs, TV commercials, magazines, books, websites, and even on the radio on the car ride home. With so many resource outlets, it's important to recognize that not all information is credible and accurate and that the best source of sports-nutrition information are qualified*

*registered dietitians, who are experts in the field of food and nutri-*
*tion. Dietitians who specialize in working with athletes have the*
*"Certified Specialist in Sports Dietetics" (CSSD) credential that*
*elevates their expertise in competitive sports-related nutritional*
*needs.*

*So, now that we've addressed what sports nutrition is, who can*
*benefit from the concepts, and where can you find evidence of these*
*principles? We should highlight some of the crucial times where*
*nutrition plays a significant role for high-level athletes. Pre- and*
*post-practice and competitions are especially suited to gaining*
*nutritional advantages. During injury, the off-season, and transi-*
*tional training periods are also recognizable nutrition peaks.*

*As you can see, sports nutrition has many stakes in an athlete's*
*development. When we consider eyesight and how important a*
*function it is in athletic performance, we have to specifically think*
*of a few select nutrients, hydration status, and energy balance. The*
*nutrients lutein, zeaxanthin, antioxidant vitamins C & E, and the*
*Omega-3 fatty acid DHA (docosahexaenoic acid) all contribute*
*to our eye health and development. One of the first signs of dehy-*
*dration is poor or blurry vision, so training and competing in a*
*hydrated state is to athletes' advantage. And just as our arms, legs,*
*etc., get tired and fatigued, so does our brain and everything it*
*controls, such as eye muscles and all that goes into our hand-eye*
*coordination. Consuming enough of the right type of energy to*
*prevent fatigue has the potential to not only fuel our major muscle*
*groups but also our eyesight. If you or your young athlete has not*
*realized the edge nutrition can provide, examining some of the*
*areas discussed above might open their eyes to another level of*
*their athletic performance!*

As you've just read from a sports nutritionist at a major
university, training, rest, and nutrition are the three pillars

of performance. I've seen how each affects the vision of elite athletes.

Nutrition is a mainstay in sports. Elite athletes know this and follow the rules.

Proper nutrition is essential to fuel the body for athletic endeavors. It ensures adequate energy to build body mass, maintain body health, fuel the body during the sport, and allows the cells and tissues to recover and rebuild after exercise and competition. Too much consumed energy, or calories, leads to an increase in body fat or muscle, and too little consumed energy leaves athletes without enough energy to meet their potential or, quite possibly, opens them up to injury and health concerns.

How do the elite athletes know what rules to follow? They do exactly what Jen Ketterly told us in her piece above: they find professional help. I know that Pete Friesen has a sports nutritionist work with the players starting on the very first day the rookies show up for camp. Each player learns about what he is putting in his body and what he has to do to supplement any deficiencies. The team provides meals for the players and, as you can imagine, there's a lot of chicken, fish, pasta, fruit, vegetables, water, and Gatorade. There are also energy bars and gels available in the locker room, and most athletes have their own supplement routine at home. (The players also are aware that some companies that provide supplements are not as reputable as others and may have tainted supplements with substances that are not allowed, so they are very particular about where they get their supplies.)

Everyone's heard the statement, "Eat your carrots; they're good for your eyes." But, how did that old tale start? Can you really eat things that will make you see better? I decided to include information about all of the nutrients that the human body uses for your eyes and vision in this book.

Here's a list of the nutrients that the eyes use, and the foods you can eat to get that specific nutrient. I believe that if athletes are eating like they should and taking supplements to make up for anything their intakes may be lacking, the eyes' needs will be adequately covered. It probably isn't necessary to add any extra supplements specifically for the eyes (though I've also included what happens to the eyes when there is a deficiency of a few of the most important nutrients).

Vitamin A

- *Eyes:* Antioxidant; helps neutralize free radicals in the chemical process of vision; helps maintain the health of the top layer of the cornea and the conjunctiva, and important in proper tear production (there are actually Vitamin A eye drops that people can use for dry eyes)
- *Foods:* Apricots, carrots, kale, mangoes, spinach, sweet potatoes
- *Deficiency:* Major cause of world blindness, night blindness, impaired vision, and dry eyes

Vitamin B2 (riboflavin)

- *Eyes:* Slows down formation of cataracts and lessens eye fatigue
- *Foods:* Meats (especially liver), eggs, milk, fortified cereals
- *Deficiency:* Red eyes (inflammation of the conjunctiva), blood vessel growth around the cornea, itching, tearing, light sensitivity, blurred vision, and cataract formation

Vitamin B6 (pyridoxine)

- *Eyes:* Important in the chemical process of tear production

- *Foods:* Lean beef, pork, poultry, tuna, oatmeal, lima beans, walnuts, peanuts, spinach, carrots, sunflower seeds
- *Deficiency:* Conjunctivitis
  Vitamin D
- *Eyes:* Anti-inflammatory and anti-angiogenic; may help decrease the chance of macular degeneration
- *Foods:* Cod liver oil, fortified milk, sardines, tuna; the best source is sunshine, though the amount you can get varies depending on where you live
- *Deficiency:* Nearsightedness

Vitamin E
- *Eyes:* Antioxidant; helps neutralize free radicals in the chemical process of vision; neuroprotective properties
- *Foods:* Beets, nuts, sunflower seeds, spinach, whole grains, wheat germ
- *Deficiency:* Eye-muscle fatigue

Minerals
   Copper, Magnesium, and Zinc
  - *Eyes:* Important in tear production; anti-inflammatory properties
  - *Foods:* Nuts, soy beans, wheat, oysters

Carotenoids
   Lutein and Zeaxanthin
  - *Eyes:* Strong antioxidant; carotenoids are yellow in color and selectively accumulate in the retina where they act as a filter for blue light, which is dangerous to the retina; may help with nighttime vision, light sensitivity, glare, and contrast sensitivity (depth perception)

- *Foods:* Spinach, kale, oranges, leaf lettuce, corn, melons, marigolds

Astaxanthin
- *Eyes:* Helps reduce photobleaching from bright lights, photo protectant, helps in focusing; anti-inflammatory properties
- *Foods:* Crab, lobster, salmon, shrimp, microalgae

Lycopene
- *Eyes:* Strong antioxidant; positive effects on blood vessel walls
- *Foods:* Tomatoes, watermelons, papayas

Flavonoids
Anthocyanins
- *Eyes:* Used in formation of rhodopsin, a chemical important in vision; useful in night vision and microcirculation
- *Foods:* Bilberries, black raspberries, blueberries, red grapes

Quercetin
- *Eyes:* Antioxidant and anti-inflammatory
- *Foods:* Apples, green tea, raspberries

Phytochemicals
Polyphenols and Catechins
- *Eyes:* Antioxidant and anti-inflammatory; help with health of blood and blood vessels
- *Foods:* Green tea

Ginkgo Flavonoids
- *Eyes:* Help ocular blood flow and microcirculation
- *Foods:* Ginkgo biloba

Phytoalexin

Resveratrol
- *Eyes:* Believed to help the retina by decreasing cholesterol and the production of fat cells
- *Foods:* Red wine (pinot noir tends to have the highest levels)

Essential Fatty Acids

Alpha-Linolenic Acid (Omega-3)
- *Eyes*: Helps in tear layer production (via the meibomian glands)
- *Foods*: Anchovies, flaxseed oil, salmon, spinach, wild cold-water fish

Linoleic Acid (Omega-6)
- *Eyes:* Anti-inflammatory
- *Food:* Canola oil, corn oil, soybean oil, sunflower oil

Other Fatty Acids

Docosahexaenoic Acid (DHA) (Omega-3)
- *Eyes*: Helps in tear production, helps corneal nerve regeneration after refractive surgery
- *Food*: Algae, cod, herring, salmon, sardines

Eicosapentaenoic Acid (Omega-3)
- *Eyes*: Improves tear production by helping the meibomian glands
- *Foods*: Algae, cod, herring, salmon, sardines

Gamma-Linolenic Acid (Omega-6)

- *Eyes*: Helps in tear production
- *Foods*: Black currant seed and borage oils, blue-green algae, hemp
  Oleic Acid (Omega-9)
- *Eyes*: Antioxidant
- *Foods*: Organic, unrefined extra virgin olive oil produced without heat

CoQ10

Enzyme found throughout the body responsible for turning fat and sugar into energy. Used by the mitochondria cells.

- *Eyes:* Believed to reduce oxidative stress in the retina; decreasing amounts are found in the eye as we age, and the thinking is that by supplementing, there can be decreased aging changes like macular degeneration

There you have it: eat for your eyes! I mentioned the old saying that carrots seem to be what you eat to help your eyes. But after reading this, I think you can see that green leafy vegetables are the eyes' best friend. As a matter of fact, it looks like you should eat a ton of spinach, throw in some nuts, and drink some red wine in order to be covered! Sorry, Mom! (My mother is a dietician, and she taught me there are no shortcuts to a well-balanced diet.)

At what age should your future elite athlete start working on nutrition? Well, you remember that in Chapter 1 we talked about how athletes in the seventh grade can be approached by college basketball recruiters. This would suggest you would want to start working on nutrition sometime before then, so that athletes will develop properly and perform to their genetic potential. Thus, it looks like we're talking elementary school age. I've already mentioned that high schools are starting to talk about nutrition. Hopefully, people will get informed so that the trend will move on to middle school-age and elementary school-age athletes.

**Eye Protection**

Sunglasses

Have you ever been to the beach on a cloudy day and ended up with a bad sunburn? That can also happen to peoples' eyes with their cheap sunglasses and knockoffs.

The sun is one of the biggest enemies of the eyes. The energy from the sun is absorbed by the tissue of different parts of the eyes and causes damage. Some of that damage is reversible and heals. Some of that damage builds up over time before causing irreparable damage. And some damage is immediate and irreversible. Here's a list of different types of damage the eye can sustain from the adverse effects of the sun:

- Pinguecula and Pterygium: These are little yellow bumps on the lining above the sclera. They are similar to calluses on our hands and grow on the eye due to sun and wind. They are usually found on the nasal-side aspect of the whites of your eyes. These must be scraped off if they grow too much.
- Photokeratitis: The cornea gets burned. This happens in snow blindness, where the intense rays of the sun bounce off the snow's surface. This also happens if you don't wear those protective shields in the tanning booth and also to welders who are not protected by a shield. Photokeratitis heals depending on how severe the burn is, but it should be treated by an eye doctor.
- Cataracts: The lens in the eye slowly yellows through long-time exposure to the sun. This is similar to the way a newspaper turns yellow when it's left out in the sun. Surgery is

eventually needed.

- Solar Retinopathy: Prolonged staring at the sun causes damage to the macula, the part of the eye used for our best vision. It's rare for this to happen on purpose; most people don't stare at the sun because it hurts their eyes. However, during a solar eclipse, the pain from looking at the sun is diminished, but the harmful rays from the sun are still present. As a result, solar retinopathy may occur in those who are not wearing protective eyewear that is stronger than regular sunglasses.

Sunglasses protect the eyes from the long-term effects of the sun. You don't have to invest a lot of money in sunglasses, but there are many options. You do need to make sure they block out the ultraviolet rays of the sun. This is where many of those low-priced knockoffs fall short. Some cheap sunglasses will make the statement that they protect you from UV rays, but when measuring absorption with a spectrometer (a machine that measures how much UV light is absorbed by the lens), you find the protection is minimal. You are definitely going to have better protection if you buy glasses made by a reputable sunglass manufacturer.

The following is a list of things to consider when picking out sunglasses (in what I believe is their order of importance):

- UV coating: Make sure it absorbs 100 percent of UVA and UVB rays.
- Lens material: Cheaper plastics can actually distort vision. Ophthalmic-grade plastics provide the best acuity.
- Tint: Pick a tint based on how you are going to use your sunglasses. Gray and green are good for general-purpose wear.

Brown usually allows for better vision in bright settings. Rose and amber allow the best depth perception and acuity for sports, but the world remains relatively bright, which can be harder on a light-sensitive athlete. Amber also blocks out blue light, which adds haze and creates visual noise. The trouble with true blue-blocking sunglasses is that depth perception can be lost, so look for lens technology that allows some red and green light in to provide better depth perception. A blue tint in glasses can help athletes complaining of photophobia or extreme light sensitivity but is not typically used in sports glasses because blue can distort images and decrease depth perception.

- Degree of light transmissibility and light rays allowed: Water sports require a darker tint than racquet sports.
- Polarized vs. nonpolarized: Pick polarized for water sports. All other sports usually are played better without polarization.
- Antireflective coating: AR coatings help decrease glare and can be put on the back surface of the lenses only or on both the front and back of the lenses.
- Mirror coating: These help reflect light more, which decreases the amount of light getting into the eyes.
- Photochromatic lenses: These lenses turn darker when you go outside and turn light when you return inside. These usually do not turn as dark when driving because the ultraviolet rays of the sun that activate the lenses are absorbed by the windshield.

Most people who don't invest in a better pair of sunglasses usually state that they are rough on sunglasses and are afraid to ruin them. People who wear the better sunglasses will tell you that there is a definite visual advantage and they have learned to take better care of the glasses. Since I'm always asked, I'll let you know that I personally wear Maui Jim and Oakley sunglasses.

Protective Sports Eyewear

When I described contact lenses in Chapter 2, I mentioned that they provide a protective covering on the cornea that can help athletes decrease the chances they get a scratch to the eye from an opponent's fingernail.

Protective eyewear that shields the eyes from injury is an important lifestyle change. It's imperative that all one-eyed or amblyopic athletes consider full-time protective eyewear to protect their good eye. Protective eyewear can add visual noise by decreasing peripheral vision or from sweat and dirt collecting on the lenses, but the benefit of safety usually outweighs these negatives.

The NHL does not mandate that athletes wear eye shields or visors when they are playing. As the eye doctor for the Carolina Hurricanes, I've tried my best to have the players wear this eye protection. I give a presentation to the rookies during their preseason training camp that shows pictures of gruesome eye injuries, and I talk about the importance of eye protection. Younger players are used to wearing eye protection because it's been mandated in every league they've been in since birth, so most of the new guys elect to continue to play wearing their eye protection. Some, and it's the taller guys usually, elect to play without protecting their eyes.

I was talking with a player on our team who had a bad eye injury as a result of a hockey stick's blade hitting his eye and scratching his cornea. The abrasion happened in an area of the cornea that didn't affect his vision, so I allowed him to play while he was healing. He was required to wear an eye shield until he recovered from his injury. Once the eye healed, I told him he had the option of wearing the visor or not, and he decided to take it off.

I asked him why.

He told me that the edge of the visor could potentially hamper his vision and give his opponent the advantage. He went on to explain that the chances for him to have the puck occurred in split-second instances. If his opponent—with no visor—has a clear view of the puck while the edge of his own visor obscures his vision of the puck and alters his reaction time, his opponent is more likely to get the puck.

I told him that he could lose an eye to an injury. Several players have had that happen, and it ended their careers.

He explained to me that for him the risk was no different than the chances he took with his knees. He could have a career-ending knee injury as a hockey player, and that was a chance he was willing to take to play hockey. So he was taking the same chances with his eyes that he was with other body parts.

One interesting note is that I get more requests for visors from football players than from athletes in any other sport. Some of these athletes complain about glare and light sensitivity. Increased glare issues and light sensitivity are associated with athletes who have sustained concussions in the past. For the majority of football players, however, I believe the request may be for other reasons, including the athletes' desire to hide their eyes from opponents or to look intimidating.

**Physical Fitness**

Another factor that influences eye health is the physical fitness of the athlete. I have noticed that preseason athletes who are in shape and athletes who are currently in their playing season perform better on visual tests. I've seen athletes at the end of the season, tired or rehabilitating from an injury or illness, test poorer with their vision than when they are in better shape or feel better. This indicates that there are physical factors that help athletes' acuity function better.

In Chapter 1, I talked about how the population of the United States is 66 percent more nearsighted than we were in the 1970s. One theory is that this shift is due to increased screen time, but another potential cause may be that we've become less active. It is my understanding that there's going to be a study to see if people who spend more time being active outside or are more fit end up less nearsighted.

### Rest

Many of us have been up late and tried to watch a movie or television when tired, only to start seeing double or to have the screen appear blurry. We usually shake our head or rub our eyes to get them working again, or we find ourselves waking up hours later wondering how the program ended.

Rest is important for the visual system to function at its peak. When fatigue sets in, the eyes are not immune to being affected like the rest of the body. Athletic performance usually isn't affected by a couple of bad evenings of sleep. But several evenings or more of poor sleep will start to catch up with an athlete. For this reason, most elite athletes keep their daily routines the same. This allows their bodies and minds to have no surprises that could cause overstimulation and interfere with sleep.

### Surround Yourself with the Right People

Successful athletes are surrounded by the right people. Successful, proactive professionals help develop successful athletes, and I think the first place that this starts is with the personal trainer or athletic trainer. Trainers need to be constantly learning and eager to tweak or change their techniques to help each individual athlete reach his or her genetic potential. I have been fortunate in my career to be involved with several such trainers and, as you know, I put Carolina Hurricanes trainer Peter Friesen at the top of the list as one of the most progressive and proactive trainers in all of sports. He's progressive in how he approaches working with athletes, including:

- The types of training they receive
- The types of therapy they receive
- His open-mindedness and constant searching for and implementation of new avenues for athletes to reach their genetic potentials
- His ability to bring together a sports-medicine team with the best providers in health care for his athletes and to "own what the providers bring to the table" by learning how those different specialties care for athletes

Pete is proactive in his approach by:

- Insuring his athletes are in peak physical shape through constantly evolving, tailor-made workouts
- Monitoring strength training so they can achieve strength while maintaining flexibility
- Making sure athletes have proper fuel for their bodies through nutritional guidance
- Finding and implementing cutting-edge techniques to help athletes reach their genetic potential
- Implementing proactive ways to help athletes avoid physical

and mental crisis

A strong and cohesive sports-medicine team works in con-
cert to provide the best possible care for athletes. I think this is
one of the most important resources an athlete can have to reach
peak performance as dictated by his or her genetic potential.
A team that is working together can direct the athlete to the
skills he or she needs to develop to compete and quite possibly
become elite. All athletes need to plan ahead to have their own
medical team or to work with a trainer who has one in place for
them.

I'm going to give you the current team of medical professionals that Pete has brought together for the Hurricanes because I
believe this will give you a better understanding of the kinds of
specialties that are represented on a good sports-medicine team.
This list includes:

Orthopaedics (from Raleigh Orthopaedic Clinic):
- Marty Isbell, MD
- Jeremy Stinson, PA-C

Primary Care (from Carolina Family Practice and Sports
Medicine):
- James Stevens, MD
- Josh Bloom, MD
- Sandeep Gavankar, DO

Dentistry:
- Tom Long, DDS
- Gabe Rich, DDS

Optometry:
- Michael Peters, OD
- Jason Price, OD

Neurosurgery:
- Robin Koeleveld, MD

Neuropsychology:
- Robert Conder, Psy.D.

Dermatology:
- Matthew Flynn, MD

General Surgery:
- Tucker Cline, MD

Cardiology:
- William Parsons, MD

Radiology:
- Steven Carter, MD

Podiatry:
- Kirk Woelffer, DPM

Chiropractic:
- Todd Staker, DC

Each one of these specialists also has a network of other great people in the medical community who they can turn to when needed to get the best supplies (such as orthotics and other equipment).

As the team optometrist, I am fortunate to have several great ophthalmologists to refer athletes to when surgical intervention is needed. They include:

- Paul Riske, MD, with a specialty in eye trauma
- Karl Stonecipher, MD, with a specialty in refractive surgery
- Raynor Casey, MD, with a specialty in retinal surgery

An extensive list of providers is available at the professional sports level and at the collegiate level, but my daughters' high school trainer, Brent Dorenkamp, is a great example of a trainer who has built a strong sports-medicine team for athletes competing at the high school level. His team includes:

- Orthopaedist Shepherd Rosenblum, MD (Triangle Orthopaedics)
- Physical therapist Chris Walters, PT
- The team of doctors at Carolina Family Medicine and Sports Practice
- Eye doctor Michael Peters, OD

During a summer high school football scrimmage game, a player lost consciousness and then his heart stopped. Dr. Rosenblum and Coach Dorenkamp were working at the game and had an automated external defibrillator (AED) with them, which allowed them to resuscitate this boy and keep him alive. The school had the AED thanks to a donation from a local hospital, REX Healthcare. A life was saved because the high school trainer had a medical team at the ready and an emergency plan in place.

Earlier we talked about the importance of nutrition to athletic performance, so a nutritionist is another member of the team who contributes to an athlete's development. I know athletes who also benefit from the work of a good massage therapist to aid in muscle recovery and range of motion. Athletes have told me that they have benefited from a close spiritual advisor as well. I would add that athletes should consider working with a sports psychologist or at least use some basic sports psychology like visualization as discussed in Chapter 8.

I hope that I've given you some insight into other details of an athlete's life that play an important role in performance and development, in reaching genetic potential, and, quite possibly, in becoming an elite athlete. It's not just happenstance. There's genetics. There are many hours of proper training and, as Jen Ketterly explained to us at the beginning of this chapter, rest and nutrition round out the three pillars of performance.

It all starts once you've learned to see to play.

# CHAPTER 10
## EYE INJURIES

Injuries are an unfortunate part of sports. Athletes can have a devastating injury to parts of their bodies such as knees and shoulders. These injuries can cause them to lose some of their physical ability on their way to trying to be elite and can even be career-ending. Athletes' eyes and visual systems are not immune from this possibility. For that reason, I am including a chapter on the eye injuries that I have seen most often in athletes accompanied by some insights into how to deal with the injuries so that athletes can return to play.

**Concussion**

The day after Christmas in 2008, Matt Cullen, then a forward for the Carolina Hurricanes, sustained a concussion from a big hit that was thrown on him in a game by an opponent on the New York Rangers. Six weeks later, he was still suffering from vision problems. He reported to the local paper, *The News & Observer*, "It's been frustrating, because physically, I feel great. I can practice fine, I can skate, I can handle the puck. I'm just having trouble seeing things on the ice normally." It took time, a change in his contact lenses, and vision exercises to help him return to normal.

Concussions are an injury to the brain. We've talked about how the eyes are a major supplier of information to the brain. Vision, and the way we see things, can get pretty messed up when

the brain is injured. Luckily, this doesn't happen with every concussion. As an eye doctor who works with elite athletes, I can
attest that this type of injury to the visual system is one of the
most stressful to the athlete, his or her team, and the medical
staff (myself included).

In Chapter 3 we talked about how expert chess players have
the ability to scan chess patterns using their peripheral vision.
We talked about how fascinating it would be to see the brain
scan of a Tom Brady or a Peyton Manning as he reads a defense,
trying to figure out the best way to attack it. And in Chapter 6 we
talked about the dorsal and ventral visual streams feeding into
the brain to give athletes information so they can make the next
move, whether it be with a conscious or a trained response.

Concussions of the visual system cause a breakdown in the
way the dorsal and ventral visual streams communicate to the
brain. And, much like a computer that gets shut down or turned
off the wrong way, it can take quite some time for the visual system to reboot after a concussion. If we could look at the brain
scans after an expert chess player or elite quarterback suffered a
concussion, I'm sure the scan would be much quieter than a scan
taken before the injury. Eye doctors play a vital role in helping
athletes reboot their visual systems.

Concussions from sports injuries are becoming far too common. The word "epidemic" has even been used when discussing
this topic. In November 2009, the general managers of the NHL
teams held meetings in Toronto to look at ways to curtail head
shots and further protect athletes. The NFL tightened rules for
return-to-play for players who suffered head injuries a month
after returning to play. In January 2010 the rules committee
for the National Federation of State High School Associations
toughened its restrictions on high school athletes who appear to

have sustained concussions. In 2011 the NFL and NHL began monitoring and updating their concussion protocols even more strictly.

As I write this book, there is concern that the cumulative effect of multiple concussions can lead to chronic traumatic encephalopathy. This condition causes changes to the brain that affect speech, thought, taste, mood, gait, and more. There is a growing concern worldwide that repeated concussions can lead to early death or to suicide in certain individuals. Players who sustained concussions during their careers, are arranging to donate their brains after death so that further research can be conducted on the cumulative effect of concussions. By doing so, they hope to aid the development of concussion diagnosis and treatment.

Carolina Family Practice and Sports Medicine is a large group medical practice in the Raleigh area with which I work closely to care for athletes who have visually related symptoms resulting from concussion. The patients who they have referred to me range from professional athletes to elementary school athletes. I've asked one of their doctors, Josh Bloom, MD, to give us some of his thoughts on this topic. Here is what he wrote:

*Nothing in sports medicine has changed more in recent years than our understanding of sports-related concussions. While comprehensively addressing the topic of sports-related concussion is beyond the scope of this book, reviewing a bit of the history of concussion management is important for a couple reasons. First, this review is illustrative regarding what we can expect in the future. Second, management of sports concussions is a great example of the collaborative "team" approach that prevails in the care of athletes and sports teams.*

*In the 1960s concussions were considered an injury to the*

*brainstem, a small structure in the brain that plays a critical role in regulating cardiac and respiratory function, the central nervous system, consciousness, and the sleep/wake cycle. Eventually, it became clear that this was not accurate; however, the focus remained on loss of consciousness (getting knocked out) as a primary indicator of the diagnosis and severity of concussion. Treatment initially included smelling salts and shaking it off and returning to play as soon as tolerated. Loss of consciousness continued as the foundation of several widely used grading scales and guidelines used in the 1980s and 1990s. However, as more data on concussions became available, it became clear that loss of consciousness actually is not a good predictor of severity of concussion. In fact, other things such as amnesia and subjective feeling of fogginess are far better predictors of severity of concussions.*

*During the late 1990s and early 2000s, increased interest, incidence, and media exposure of sports concussions led to more critical study of the condition. Three times between 2001 and 2008, a group of international thought leaders from a variety of medical specialties convened to extensively review the medical literature on concussions in sports in an effort to answer many of the pressing clinical questions about diagnosis, management, and potential short- and long-term impact of this injury. After each of these conferences, a consensus statement was released to disseminate information and provide guidance in the diagnosis and management of concussions.*

*Interestingly, as more and more data came to light, each successive meeting of this international conference concluded with progressively more and more conservative recommendations regarding what constitutes a concussion and when it is safe to return to sport. For example, initially it was the standard of care to return players to sport if all symptoms resolved within 20 minutes after the injury. Now, it is widely accepted that an athlete with a concussion should not return to play the same day, period. In fact, most young athletes are not returned to full competition for at least one week, often longer.*

*With the help of this group and others, we have moved away from a relatively rigid "cookbook" approach to managing concussions to a highly individualized approach. Concussion assessment now involves inquiring about a wide variety of symptoms, examining the patient comprehensively for neurological, balance, memory, visual, and cognitive deficits acutely after the injury and again at intervals over time. We have learned that certain patient characteristics and medical conditions such as youth, history of previous concussions, migraines, motion sickness, anxiety or depression, and attention deficit disorder seem to be associated with prolonged and more severe concussions. Sadly, it is also becoming painfully clear that concussions, particularly multiple concussions, can lead to devastating long-term sequelae, such as premature dementia, severe depression and anxiety, chronic headaches, and increased risk of suicidality in certain individuals. We have learned of the importance of cognitive rest and physical rest in the management of concussions and armed ourselves with tools to better assess severity of injury and most importantly when, and if, athletes are safely able to return to sport. Neuropsychological testing is one of the many tools now utilized to help with what is often the most difficult part of concussion management: deciding when the concussion has resolved entirely.*

*Many athletes have subclinical neurocognitive deficits (i.e., the athlete feels fine, is completely asymptomatic, but the brain has still not healed entirely). It is unsafe (and can lead to catastrophic outcomes) if an athlete is returned to play prior to complete resolution of the concussion. In these instances, neuropsychological testing is often a helpful tool. The most widely used neuropsychological test is called ImPACT and is used by teams and athletes from junior high to the NHL, NFL, and MLB. These tests help to quantify and assess things like focus, concentration, verbal memory, visual memory, and reaction time. Ideally, athletes will have a baseline test prior to the season, and this is compared with postinjury scores after a concussion. If postinjury scores are below baseline scores, even if an athlete no longer has any symptoms of concussion, it is not safe for them to return to play. This is just one example of a growing number of tools at the disposal of physicians to help with management of sports-related concussions.*

*Arguably as much as any aspect of medicine, sports medicine embraces a team approach to care for athletes, teams, and organizations. Concussion management is the perfect illustration of this team approach. Identification of concussions is often done on the sideline when no physician is present. In a high school setting, this diagnosis and initial management is often done by a certified athletic trainer. These well-trained, college-educated professionals are highly proficient at identifying and providing initial management of the multitude of injuries that can be seen on fields, courts, rinks, mats, and so forth. Once identified, athletes with concussions are removed from play and given instructions for strict physical and cognitive rest and often referred to a physician who collaborates with the certified athletic trainer (and other providers if needed) for definitive care.*

*I work in a 12-provider, three-clinic family practice and sports-medicine group. We provide coverage to athletes of all ages and abilities throughout the greater Raleigh metro area. In 2008 we opened Carolina Sports Concussion Clinic. We now see over 700 new concussions per year. Approximately 80 percent of the concussions we see resolve with neurocognitive rest within three weeks.*

*However, some take longer and require more active treatment. In these cases, we generally see more complicated injury patterns, including injuries to the visual pathways and vestibular system. [For these situations] we obtain help from our concussion team, including sports-minded eye specialists such as Dr. Mike Peters, vestibular therapists, sports psychologists, and physical therapists.*

*Many concussions have a visual component. Like most other symptoms and deficits, most of these resolve spontaneously within a matter of days. However, we learned (largely from our experience with several elite-level hockey players) that these abnormalities in the visual pathway are often quite difficult for patients to describe. However, once they are identified, these deficits are typically quite amenable to visual therapy and corrective-lens solutions. This is often some of the most gratifying and rapid improvement seen in the often slow and tedious process of concussion recovery.*

*One remarkable case involved an NHL player who sustained a concussion and said, "[I'm] feeling good, but something is still off." We quickly had him evaluated, and he was found to be entirely neglecting his left eye (very similar to a child with amblyopia, the condition seen in children where the brain neglects one eye that does not see as well as the other and can lead to a lazy eye if untreated). Over the course of this player's optometric evaluation, his brain realized it was not using the left eye and simply flipped the switch and engaged the left eye. His symptoms resolved, and he was back to baseline by the time he left his optometric evaluation. Obviously, not all cases are this dramatic, but it is clear from other cases if these deficits are not identified, they can lead to persistent and prolonged symptoms.*

*In the years to come, we can expect our understanding of sports-related concussions to continue to grow tremendously and our management of these injuries to remain dynamic. We will have*

*more tools at our disposal and be able to better educate athletes
and their families on the risks of sports and allow appropriate
diagnosis, treatment, and safe return-to-play. Ultimately, a collaborative, team-based approach utilizing the expertise of many
health care providers will optimize the safety and performance of
these athletes.*

I hope that you gain a better understanding of how real and
potentially dangerous concussions can be from reading what Dr.
Bloom wrote. I know most of you involved with athletics have
more than likely experienced this with a player around you. I
think you also see that it's important to have a team of doctors
ready to help athletes recuperate. As discussed in the previous
chapter, I want to again emphasize how important it is for the
trainer on the front lines to be networked with a group of doctors who work well as a team in the effort to care for athletes.

To break down concussions and teach you about them in a
little more detail, I can use an illustration where the brain is like
a big mansion with many rooms. Each one of these rooms has
electricity in it to run the lights, television, stereo, clock radio,
etc. There is a major electrical box in the utility room and each
breaker on the board represents one of the rooms. A concussion
is like a big electrical storm of lightning hitting the house and
sending a shockwave into the electrical system so that some or
even all of the breakers flip. A flipped breaker causes the electricity to be turned off in a room. In order to get the house's
electricity back up and running, those breaker switches each
have to be turned on again.

The rooms in the brain include a room for speech, a room
for vision, a room for smell, a room for thought, a room for
short-term memory, a room for long-term memory, a room to
run an arm, a room to run a leg. I think you get the idea.

When the head is hit, an electrical shock wave causes the "breakers" to blow (what's referred to as a *diffuse axonal injury*). Sometimes the breakers are turned back on quickly and the rooms get going again. Other times, the breakers may take a long time to turn back on or possibly never turn back on. This is why people may stutter for a while, may have memory loss for a while, and may have lasting numbness in a certain part of the body, such as an arm. People may even see the world "move funny" and not be able to make any sense of their vision.

Not all concussions affect the visual system. Dr. Bloom mentioned the ImPACT test. As he stated, this is a test that athletes perform preseason to give doctors information on brain function, which is then used as each individual athlete's baseline. In the event that an athlete suffers a concussion, the doctor looks at the athlete's preseason brain-function levels and compares it to test findings after the injury. This tool gives measurable findings that can be used for comparative purposes and to better understand the athlete's injury.

For brain injuries that affect the visual system, I'd like to give you specifics. But our knowledge is ever-evolving as we continue to learn more about this type of injury. My intention is not to say that any of these things are "definites" but rather to give you an idea of the direction where we are headed in our learning and treatment philosophies.

Eye doctors can also run preseason tests on athletes to record the preconcussive state of an athlete's visual system. If necessary, the eye doctor can test again and discover whether a decrease in a visual finding has been caused by a visually related concussion. Findings for subsequent tests can be monitored for improvement as the athlete heals. This type of information is a valuable part in the overall evaluation and decision-making process regarding an athlete's recovery and return-to-play status. The eye doctor's role is pivotal in facilitating the recovery of the athlete's visual system. For that reason, I've been very excited to have a personal role in helping elite athletes return back to form.

The symptoms that an athlete reports to me usually indicate whether their vision is involved. Double vision, blurred vision, trouble focusing, and seeing flashing lights are common reports. Most athletes report that the world seems to move differently. They tend to notice this more when riding in cars. Many athletes report that they get an anxious and light-headed feeling when going into a crowd of people. Several athletes have mentioned that when they return to the arena to watch games, the strobe lights and loud noises make them feel funny. When cleared for physical activity, they may continue to report feeling overwhelmed by visual input.

I want to include a list of effects a concussion can have on the visual system. (Remember, this is such a new world of study that it is continually evolving.)

Visual Acuity

Best-corrected visual acuity may worsen by a line or two. The athlete who was 20/15 may become 20/25 post-concussion. This is a reason for a full change in their spectacle prescription, no matter how small the difference.

I have noticed a tendency for most athletes to shift in a more farsighted (or less nearsighted) direction from their preconcussion prescription. An increase in astigmatism is noted in the overwhelming majority of cases. Regardless, athletes seem to thrive on wearing the maximum prescription, no matter how small the shift. It appears that as the brain is rebooting the visual system, the eyes don't want to work hard to see. The new prescription seems to relax the visual system so that athletes don't suffer as much eye strain or eye-related headaches. A blue tint in glasses helps those athletes complaining of photophobia or extreme light sensitivity.

## Suppression

Suppression of one eye (meaning the brain has turned that eye's "switch" off and ignores its input) may occur and is most often intermittent. The eye on the side of the hit is usually the eye that is affected. I use a test called the Worth 4-dot test to check for any type of suppression. The Worth 4-dot test seems to give the examiner the best reading on suppression. The image seen during this test by an eye that is intermittently suppressed may seem to twirl, shake, or move. This is evidence that the dorsal visual stream is throwing off the inner ear or vice versa. In most cases when an athlete complains of the world moving too fast, intermittent suppression seems to be the culprit.

As Dr. Bloom mentioned, one of the Hurricanes with a visually related concussion had this type of problem, and his suppression faded away within a couple of hours of his eyes being tested.

## Jerky Eye Movements

Pursuits and saccades can be erratic. Poor eye movement is one of the most common visual problems of concussed athletes. Evaluating athletes for this problem is now used on the sidelines to aid in early diagnosis. I test for this as well and recommend exercises to correct any problems.

## Pupil Size/Response

The pupils and iris muscle function may be altered. This

is usually because the focusing or accommodation system isn't working properly. I document individual pupil size on preseason physicals so that this can be checked during times of injury.

### Accommodative Dysfunction

The accommodative system seems to be most commonly affected by brain injury. Monocular issues have to be restored before binocularity work can be performed. Home and in-office exercises are often prescribed. The doctor has to be careful that the athlete doesn't obsess over this training, because overtraining can paradoxically delay the improvement of the dorsal visual stream.

### Convergence/Divergence Issues

Decreased convergence and sluggish divergence are common issues. Exercises can be given to help restore proper muscle function.

### Depth Perception and Spatial Issues

Depth perception may be decreased if fusion is decreased or intermittent suppression is involved. An explanation may be that one eye is affected more by the incident than the other, especially when suppression is present. As the monocular issue resolves, binocularity and perceptual functioning are restored, resulting in improved depth perception.

### Eye-Hand-Body Coordination/Reaction

Concussed athletes usually report that they feel like they're moving slower. There have even been tests designed to measure the decrease in eye-hand reaction speed. One such test is a grasp test that uses a stick that is around three feet long with a hockey puck attached at one end. A tester holds the stick at the end away from the puck while the athlete is directed to hold one hand at the ready around the stick near the end with the puck. On a count of three, the tester releases the stick and the athlete is supposed to grab the stick as fast as he or she can as gravity causes the puck to fall toward the floor. Athletes with concussions that affect the visual system don't grasp the stick as fast as they did before the injury.

Pete Friesen and I use ball exercises to aid in rehabilitation. Care must be taken to use indirect gaze as opposed to the athlete fixating on the ball.

## Midline Shift

This occurs when the athlete's perception of his or her body's middle shifts off to the left or right. Athletes with a midline shift tend to walk down a hallway awkwardly close to one wall or the other. I have a test for athletes to perform to help diagnose when this problem is present.

## Perceptual Issues (Visual Memory)

Many perceptual issues are caught by current concussion testing, such as the ImPACT Test. I run tests that confirm this finding. This testing is especially helpful to evaluate progress and improvement as return-to-play is considered. The King-Devick test has gained a lot of favor recently, and I have found it very useful as well.

## Balance and Proprioception

This is the area that is usually involved when athletes complain of the world moving too fast or if they feel overwhelmed by visual input when they are getting back to game speed. I use exercises incorporating prisms, a balance board, strobe lights, and strobe glasses to aid in recovery.

Visual Field

Visual field testing can reveal a decrease in peripheral vision.

When an athlete is referred to me for evaluation, I have to be sure that the athlete is able to withstand the testing. Sometimes the athlete is unable to go through the testing because the brain is too injured. Athletes in this state usually report no problems with their vision, but when I try to start the testing, they can't do it, shake their heads, and drop out quickly. These athletes may report they are tired, that their heads feel funny, or that they are beginning to feel dizzy. When this occurs, testing should stop until the brain has had more time to heal.

For my post-concussion work with professional athletes, I have been fortunate that our team of doctors tests their visual skills during the preseason. We have a good starting point on how an athlete's visual system functions under normal circumstances and can determine what part is broken. After determining which part of the visual system is affected, we use that as the starting place for rehabilitation and recovery.

The exercises and rehabilitation that I use to help athletes recover are determined by which part of the visual pathway is not working correctly. These are the same types of exercises that I use in vision therapy. I usually have the athlete return to my office two to three times per week. The athlete is also given exercises to take home to perform. As the athlete is cleared for physical exertion, these visual exercises move on to the playing field and are incorporated into their normal sports tasks. My team and I work closely with the athletic trainer at this point to help facilitate the remaining rehabilitation.

I started this chapter with concussions because these are one of the most common injuries with which I work. I will next discuss other injuries I commonly see and then end the chapter with a discussion of the injuries that I don't see as frequently.

### Corneal Injuries

Scratches to the cornea are the next-most-common injury that I treat. The cornea is rich with nerve fibers, so when someone gets something in his or her eye, it's very noticeable, and if the cornea gets scratched, the resulting pain can become excruciating. The best treatment before getting to the eye doctor is putting in artificial tears. This creates a barrier between the scratch and the eyelid and helps soothe the pain. Keeping the eye closed is sometimes the best treatment. This injury should also be evaluated as soon as possible. Some injuries can actually penetrate the cornea (meaning a hole gets punched completely through the cornea), which allows the *aqueous* fluid from inside the eyeball to seep out. If enough fluid leaks out, permanent vision loss can occur or the athlete can lose the eye completely.

---

*See to Play Tip 16:*
*Never allow an athlete to push on*
*his or her eye when in severe pain.*

---

The reasoning behind this See to Play Tip is that if a penetrating injury is present, the eye injury may be severe enough that the act of putting pressure on it will make things worse. Putting pressure on an injured eye could actually cause fluid to leak out from the inside of the eyeball.

As I've mentioned, athletes who wear contact lenses when

playing are less likely to have corneal abrasions. This is because the contact lens acts as a protective barrier to the cornea. When a fingernail or object flies in the eye, it hits the contact lens first, often damaging it or causing it to pop out. This is the primary reason basketball players lose contact lenses while playing, and you often see them on their knees looking on the court for the lost lens. This might be a nuisance, but the lens actually saved the cornea from being abraded and the athlete from ending up in terrible pain.

I almost exclusively use contact lenses to treat corneal abrasions. As a matter of fact, if the abrasion happens during a game, I'll numb the eye with a topical medication and put a contact lens in place, which acts like a bandage. If the abrasion is not in the center of the cornea and the visual acuity is not affected, the player can usually return to play.

### External Eye Injuries

External eye injuries are the next-most-common eye injury and usually the most gruesome-looking. You know the story: the dreaded black eye. Blunt trauma from an outside source hits the eyelid, causing tissue damage and blood vessels to rupture. Blood pools under the skin of the eyelid, and a black eye forms. Compression and ice are needed as soon as possible to decrease swelling. (So, get that steak out of the freezer and slap it on your eyes like they do in movies, or be like Rocky and yell, "Cut me Mick!" when the eye is completely closed shut from blood pooling in the eyelids. I'm joking—but you really should get a cold compress on the eye until it can be evaluated professionally.)

The eyeball is housed in a room made of bone known as the orbit. If you look at a picture of a skull, you can see that room. The portion that is part of the face is known as the orbital rim.

SEE TO PLAY                                    201

In the inside of the orbit there are walls. The walls include the side by the nose, the outside wall toward the ear, the floor, the back wall, and the roof.

Those bones can be injured by blunt trauma. There can be a fracture of the rim that surrounds the outer lining of the room. I examined a USA National Baseball team infielder who sustained this type of injury. He was fielding a ball that was hit on the ground and rolling to him at a high rate of speed. The ball took a bad bounce up toward his face, then hit and cracked his orbital rim.

A major complication from this type of injury is that one or more of the muscles that move the eyeball can get hooked up in the crack if it's big enough. An athlete who has an orbital-rim fracture may be able to play during the healing process if the fracture is relatively minor and he or she wears a facial shield while participating. This shield is similar to the type of shield used for athletes who have broken their noses or fractured another bone of the face.

Trauma can produce a high amount of pressure inside the orbit, which may result in a crack or break of one or more of the orbital walls. The ethmoid bone is the thinnest bone in the orbit, and it comprises the nasal aspect of the orbit. This bone is very thin and can crack or have a hole punched in it when the right amount of force or pressure is applied within the orbit. The athlete will usually feel air moving into the eye area when he or she blows his nose. Surgery is usually needed to correct this but not always. Athletes with this type of injury should not be allowed to travel in airplanes until it heals.

I had a gentleman show up in my office one morning after getting a fist to his eye the previous day. He was explaining to me that he felt air near his hurt eye. He reported that his eyelid puffed up when he blew his nose to clear the blood out of his sinuses. His girlfriend related that he had passed out after blowing his nose the night before and once in the car ride after the fight.

"Yeah, Doc. Watch," he said as he went to blow his nose to show me.

I tried to stop him, but it was too late! He blew his nose, causing his top and bottom eyelids to blow up like a balloon. This act created so much pain that it threw his body into shock and he started having a seizure on the spot. Needless to say, he went straight to the hospital after my team and I got him stable.

The orbit floor can break when the pressure inside the orbit exceeds what the floor can handle. The orbital floor is the most common area for an orbital fracture. This causes the eyeball to drop down, which produces double vision. (It's just like in a movie where you see a person fall through a hole in the floor and get stuck halfway through.) This kind of fracture is also called an *orbital blowout fracture*, as the eye falls back and down into the orbit. This injury requires surgery to prevent permanent complications. The surgeon repairs the area of the break and then puts in plates to build the floor back up. This allows the eye to go back to its normal position. Once repositioned, the eyes may be slightly out of the alignment that they were pre-surgery. Eye doctors can design exercises to help the eyes learn to work as a team again.

One player on the Hurricanes had this type of injury and surgery. He was playing in a game and one of the players on the other team took a swing at him with his hockey glove still on. The thumb of the glove hit his eye so hard that it pushed the eye down and blew out the orbital floor. The doctors rebuilt the floor with little plates so that the eye moved back to its normal position. He did so well with the surgery that he was allowed to play again after recovering.

That player didn't have any problems with his eye or injury until about three years after the surgery. He started noticing that he was seeing two of everything when he looked up the ice if his chin was in a downward position pushed against his chest. Sure enough, after testing his eye alignment and muscle function, I noticed that his eyes weren't working together well on upward gaze. I recommended Pencil Push-Up exercises to get those eye muscles back into shape, and his double vision went away.

The eye muscles that move the eyeballs can be injured as well. They may get cut, in which case surgery is required to fix them, or the muscles that turn the eye in or out may not fully function. As I noted above, eye muscles can also get caught in the cracks of a fracture to the orbital walls, which will cause them to stick or move in a jerky fashion. Damage to the nerve that controls the eye muscles may also occur. Nerve damage can cause the eyelid to malfunction so that it does not close fully, which dries out the cornea.

Injuries to the external eye need to be looked at by a physician when:

- Swelling of the eyelid completely shuts the eye
- There is a lot of pain, especially at the site of impact
- The eye does not move evenly, sees double, or gets stuck in position
- There is a large cut that needs stitches to close and heal
- The athlete hears or feels air around the eye socket
- Anytime you are concerned. It is better to be safe than sorry!

## Internal Eye Injuries

The iris is the blue-, brown-, or green-colored part of the eye. It can get injured with direct force to the eyeball. The immediate injury can be that it rips or bleeds. When this happens, blood will actually float in the fluid in front of the colored part of the eye. This is a serious injury. Athletes injured in this fashion should keep their head upright or in an inclined position until they can get to a specialist to be evaluated. In most cases, the blood resolves on its own without treatment, but medicines are usually given to make the eye more comfortable and speed up the healing process. There is always a concern that the pressure inside the eye will change greatly, which can cause significant complications.

During a hockey game, a puck hit a player in the eye. The majority of the force hit his orbital rim, but the remaining force hit the eyeball, causing a rip in his iris. The result was a pool of blood in the fluid inside of his eye. When he bent down to take off his skate, the blood covered his pupil and he temporarily lost all vision in that eye. Needless to say, he became very worried. He had to sit out for about a week while the eye healed. He ended up with no vision loss. He's monitored yearly to make sure that complications such as glaucoma don't develop.

The iris can get bruised and become swollen; this condition is referred to as iritis. Iritis is very painful, and the eye becomes very red and the athlete becomes very light-sensitive. A high school lacrosse player who was a patient of mine had a bad iritis injury. One day before practice started, he was hanging out on the sidelines and was not wearing his eye protection. Two other players were passing the ball as they were running onto the field. The ball bounced up and hit my patient in the eye and created a tremendous iritis or bruise of the middle eye. This injury was so bad that he had to have an injection of steroids administered to the outside lining of the eye so that the eye would heal and the inflammation would go away. This injury took a long time to heal, and the athlete was fortunate that there was no permanent vision loss.

A sphincter muscle controls the pupil, or black center of the iris. This muscle can also become injured. This type of injury can cause the athlete to have a misshapen pupil, or quite possibly the pupil won't constrict much at all. It may even stay in a dilated position. This causes the athlete to be light sensitive until it heals. Vision will be affected with objects appearing to have a halo or glow around them. Focusing (accommodation) can be decreased with this type of injury. The muscle that keeps our pupil small also can start cramping, resulting in browache pain. To treat this, eye doctors give steroid drops as well as dilate the eye to relax the cramping muscles.

A doctor should evaluate any injury that affects the pupil immediately, especially if the pupil is "blown" or significantly larger than normal. Brain injuries can sometimes present themselves with a pupil that doesn't respond normally. Time is of the essence in these cases for quick and appropriate diagnosis and treatment.

A long-term problem associated with iris injuries is that affected athletes can develop glaucoma later in life. There is a drainage system at the root of the iris that helps regulate the fluid in the eyeball. Debris and pigment from an injury can clog up this drain or cause it to malfunction. When that happens, the pressure inside the eyeball goes up and causes the optic nerve to die out. Kirby Puckett was a well-known Major League Baseball player who experienced this traumatic injury. A ball hit him in the eye during his playing career. Later in life, he developed glaucoma and went blind. Athletes who have had this type of eye injury should be tested at least once a year for glaucoma for the rest of their lives. If caught in time, blindness can be avoided.

Behind the iris, there is a lens that allows us to focus in order to see clearly. This lens bulges in and out like a camera lens zooms in and out. The lens in the eye can also sustain an injury. If the muscles that are in charge of focusing are injured, the eye will lose its ability to focus clearly and quickly. The lens can turn yellow or opaque from trauma, which is known as a traumatic cataract. If the injury is severe enough, the lens can be dislodged from the muscles that hold it and it can float to the back part of the eye.

The vitreous is the fluid found behind the lens. It is a clear fluid, but injury can cause debris and blood to float in this area. Minor changes in the vitreous can create what are known as floaters. Here, the athlete will see black spots floating around. These move as the eye moves and swing back and forth but are usually minor and do not require surgery. An injury that is bad enough to cause the vitreous to turn hazy will require surgery to remove this fluid and have new fluid put in its place.

An athlete who starts seeing a black dot floating around in one eye every now and then is usually not a medical emergency but should be evaluated by an eye doctor at some point. If the athlete sees multiple black dots floating around, (say, more than 10), the athlete should schedule an appointment. An athlete who describes seeing a curtain falling into his or her vision or who actually sees fireworks going off in her eyes should call the eye doctor immediately for an urgent evaluation.

In Chapter 3 I described the retina, which is in the back of the eye and holds the photoreceptors that are responsible for vision. There can be several types of injuries to this area.

First, there can be blood-vessel injuries to the retina. A *Valsalva maneuver* can cause hemorrhages to the blood vessels in the retina. This can occur when an athlete lifts a large amount of weight, as in a heavy weight-lifting squat or clean and jerk, while holding his or her breath. This causes a sharp rise in intrathoracic or intra-abdominal blood pressure, which causes a sudden rise in the intraocular venous pressure and can result in a rupture of the superficial retinal capillaries. The resultant blood may pool in the inner layers of the retina or actually leak out into the vitreous fluid. Surgery may be needed if there is a significant amount of bleeding. The retina can swell due to blunt trauma to the eyeball as well. If the energy of the injury is trans-ferred to the retina, it causes it to swell (similar to a bruise). This can cause the athlete's vision to become distorted. Things start to appear more bowed or wavy. Athletes may also perceive this as a gray area of haze that they cannot see through, like a bubble in their vision. This hazy area will stay constant in all areas of gaze and will not float around the way floaters in the vitreous do.

There is usually not much pain associated with a retinal-swelling injury unless there are other parts of the eye involved. These injuries typically seem to get better on their own, but doctors usually follow them closely to make certain leakage or retinal breaks don't occur.

Trauma can also cause the retina tissue to pull off of the back of the eye. This is known as a retinal detachment. The athlete will see bright flashing lights going off in the eye like fireworks and have trouble seeing clearly with the affected eye. Immediate attention is needed to reattach the retina. This type of injury is usually free of pain but is an emergency situation.

Some people have retinal detachments spontaneously or without trauma. This is usually due to weaknesses that are already present in their retinas. Thinned areas of the retina can lead to detachments. Athletes should have a dilated eye exam every year at their eye doctor's office to ensure there are no areas of retinal weakness. If retinal holes or tears are present, surgery may be needed to correct those areas so that athletes can return to their sports again someday.

I hope this chapter has helped you learn more about the different types of eye injuries that can occur in sports. Most people who find themselves around eye injuries usually feel a little squeamish. For that reason, I hope that because I've taught you what to expect from eye injuries, you will feel calmer when they occur; this should also help you feel more confident in providing appropriate care for your athlete.

# CHAPTER 11
## EARLY CAREER EXERCISES

This chapter describes exercises that are geared especially toward young athletes, ideally between three and eight years of age. These exercises also work for older children who are beginning to build their vision skills for the first time. Older children may be able to master the skills in these exercises more quickly, but it is still important to spend time at each level before adding variations or difficulty, just as one should climb up stairs one at a time to prevent a fall.

As the father of three children, I understand the time constraints on a family's day. However, I believe that this type of vision training is vital to the overall development of a child as both student and athlete and that it should be incorporated into his or her daily routine. A properly working visual system is the basic foundation for both sports and learning, and throughout this book you have read about the deficiencies that can interfere with success. Therefore, you should view the 20 minutes you spend each day on this training as a two-for-one special—as though a coach were spending 20 minutes with your child teaching the fine art of shooting a basketball and a math tutor were spending 20 minutes with your child teaching multiplication tables.

I also understand family budget constraints. These exercises use equipment that can be made out of items found around your home or that is inexpensive to purchase. Many of the items you can use for training can also be found on my website at www. seetoplay.com if you find them hard to make yourself.

As I describe the exercises, I refer to the child as "the athlete." More than likely, it will be a parent who fills the other role in these exercises, as the trainer.

Each exercise is assigned to a group based on the aspect of vision that it works. The groups are:

> EM: **E**ye-**M**uscle **M**ovement
>
> V: **V**ergence (Convergence and Divergence)
>
> F: **F**ocusing
>
> P: **P**eripheral Awareness
>
> EH: **E**ye-**H**and-Body Coordination
>
> ME: **M**ind's **E**ye

Some exercises are assigned to more than one group. You can add these exercises to the practice schedule when an exercise from either group is called for.

### Practice Schedule

I recommend that young athletes perform their vision exercises at the same time every weekday (for example, after school from 4:00 to 4:20 pm) so that it becomes a daily routine. I also recommend that the athletes train their eyes for a period of nine weeks and then take a three-week break.

The daily schedule can vary as follows:

<u>Monday-Wednesday-Friday</u>
- 5 minutes of one exercise from group EM
- 5 minutes of one exercise from group V
- 5 minutes of one exercise from group F
- 5 minutes of one exercise from group P

<u>Tuesday-Thursday</u>
- 10 minutes of one exercise from group EH
- 10 minutes of one exercise from group ME

Use the chart below like a menu to help you design your daily and weekly workouts. Try to use each of the exercises before you start to repeat them. The exercises are explained in full throughout the rest of the chapter.

## Exercise Menu

|                                   | EM | V | F | P | EH | ME |
|-----------------------------------|----|---|---|---|----|----|
| Flashlight Tag                    | X  |   |   |   |    |    |
| Follow the Ball                   | X  |   | X |   |    |    |
| Beanbag Toss                      | X  |   |   |   |    |    |
| Pirate Patch Beanbag Toss         | X  |   |   |   |    |    |
| Paper Towel Roll                  | X  |   |   |   |    |    |
| Table Exercise                    |    | X |   |   |    |    |
| Two Pennies Three                 |    | X |   |   |    |    |
| Penny Christmas Tree              |    | X |   |   |    |    |
| Creep Up a String                 |    | X |   |   |    |    |
| Card Focus                        |    |   | X |   |    |    |
| Peripheral Awareness              |    |   |   | X |    |    |
| Eraser Board Circles and Squares  |    |   |   | X |    |    |
| Scrabble Piece Side-Vision Game   |    |   |   | X |    |    |
| Bounce a Ball and Catch           |    |   | X |   | X  |    |
| Bounce a Ball and Turn Around     |    |   |   |   | X  |    |
| Bounce a Ball and Hit with a Stick|    |   |   |   | X  |    |
| Juggling                          |    |   |   |   | X  |    |
| Soccer Ball/Hacky Sack Juggle     |    |   |   |   | X  |    |
| Two-Card Remember                 |    |   |   |   |    | X  |
| Three/Four-Card Game              |    |   |   |   |    | X  |
| Monopoly Piece Memory Game        |    |   |   |   |    | X  |
| Scrabble Piece Memory Game        |    |   |   |   |    | X  |

## Log Sheets

Use the following charts as log sheets for your weekly exercises. Before you begin Monday's exercises, fill out the sheet completely with all the exercises you intend to perform. Make sure you try to incorporate all the different exercises before you start to repeat them. Also, check off the exercises after you have finished so that you have a good record of all the exercises you have performed. (I will also make log sheets available to download from my website www.seetoplay.com.)

| | Monday | Tuesday | Wednesday | Thursday | Friday |
|---|---|---|---|---|---|
| **EM** 5 minutes | | n/a | | n/a | |
| **V** 5 minutes | | n/a | | n/a | |
| **F** 5 minutes | | n/a | | n/a | |
| **P** 5 minutes | | n/a | | n/a | |
| **EH** 10 minutes | n/a | | n/a | | n/a |
| **ME** 10 minutes | n/a | | n/a | | n/a |

## Exercises

### Flashlight Tag

Group: EM

Objective: To develop the fine motor movements of the muscles that move the eyes

Equipment needed: Masking tape, two flashlights

Instructions: This exercise is a warm-up as well as a means of conditioning the eye muscles. It is a two-part exercise. It is important to do these parts in order. Part one is for warming up and improving motor skill. Part two focuses on strengthening extreme gaze.

Note: For smaller athletes, finding a platform that they can stand on to get eye level to approximately five feet will help give them a larger area to move their eyes.

Part One: Warm-Up and Motor Skill

Use masking tape to place an *X* that is at eye level to your athlete in the middle of a large wall. It can be a foot or two higher but not much more than that.

The athlete and trainer both need a flashlight in one hand. They need to stand side by side facing the $X$, preferably with their backs against a wall, at least 15 feet away. The athlete is not allowed to move his or her head throughout the entire exercise, only his eyes.

Both athlete and trainer start with their flashlights shining on the $X$. The trainer slowly moves the flashlight so that the light goes up to the top left corner of the wall. The athlete follows the light by moving only his eyes. (For our shorter or younger athletes, their vertical-gaze limit may be exceeded when the spot is all the way at the top of the wall. The trainer will have to adjust the "top" of this exercise to a level more like three-fourths of the way up the wall.) Our athlete also uses his flashlight to follow and tag the trainer's light. The trainer now begins a zigzag pattern all over the wall. It is important to start slow for the first minute. The trainer can then switch to a circular pattern, going clockwise first. The trainer can make the circles smaller and smaller and can switch to a counterclockwise rotation at any time. Randomly change back and forth, from the zigzag to the circle pattern and back again, for the next two minutes.

The trainer can increase the speed after the first minute of the exercise. The goal is to build a full range of eye-muscle motion and also very fine motor movement by using small patterns as well as larger ones. Building speed is not one of the goals, but the pace should be changed from time to time so that this drill is more fun for the athlete.

Another way to modify this exercise after the first minute is to allow the athlete to change the fixation of his eyes from the trainer's spot to his own spot and then, after 20 seconds or so, back to the trainer's spot. The trainer is in control of this by saying, "My spot." This means the athlete's gaze is fixated on the trainer's spot. When the trainer says, "Your spot," the athlete changes fixation to his own flashlight spot.

The patterns can also go down onto the floor and close to our athlete. Be sure that the patterns remain within the gaze of the athlete (who is still not moving his head!) throughout the entirety of the exercise.

Part Two: Jump to It!

The trainer challenges the athlete to use more extreme gaze points in this part of the exercise. The athlete starts by looking at the $X$ on the wall. The trainer starts with the flashlight off, points it to a spot on the wall that would be in an extreme side area of gaze for the athlete, and then turns on the flashlight. When this happens, the athlete must "jump" his flashlight's light to tag the trainer's spot. The athlete's eyes travel to the spot along with his light. The trainer turns off her flashlight, points it at a different part of the wall in another direction, and flashes the light back on. The athlete moves his eyes to look at that spot and tags the light again.

In this part of the exercise, increasing the speed is important. It is also important for the athlete to place his flashlight spot and eye gaze accurately on the trainer's spot. Note that the trainer may need to stand behind the athlete so that the athlete doesn't use his side vision to get clues as to where the trainer is moving the flashlight spot.

Variations: As the athlete becomes proficient in this exercise, begin to incorporate the following variations to increase the level of difficulty. Begin at the top of the list, master a variation, and then move on to the next level of difficulty.

- Have the athlete stand on one foot from time to time.
- Ask the athlete to close one eye from time to time.
- Balance a book on the athlete's head.
- Tell athlete to run in place.
- Tell athlete to jump in place.
- Ask the athlete to sit or lie on the floor.
- Have the athlete lie on their back, head down (upside down) on a couch.
- Bounce a tennis ball off the wall so that it rolls to the athlete. The athlete still needs to fixate on the spot but also has to try to touch the ball with one foot.
- Have the athlete bounce on a mini trampoline.

**Follow the Ball**

Group: EM or F

Objective: To develop fine motor movements of the eye muscles and improve accommodation

Equipment: A hanging ball

This exercise requires a little setup. You can make your own hanging ball by inserting an eyelet screw into a hard plastic baseball or softball (similar to a Wiffle ball) and tying a 15-foot piece of kite string to the screw. Use a marker to draw letters and numbers that are one inch high on the ball.

Instructions: Attach the other end of the string to the ceiling so that the ball height starts at the athlete's eye level. Have the athlete stand from three to five feet from the ball. Swing the ball in a manner such that it moves from left to right for the full length of the athlete's range of gaze. Again, the athlete should not move his head during this exercise, only his eyes. The athlete should also try to read as many different letters or numbers as he can on the ball during the exercise. Continue to read and call out the letters and numbers for one to two minutes.

Next, swing the ball directly toward the athlete (without hitting him). The ball should travel back and forth while the athlete again reads and calls out the different letters for one to two minutes.

Next, increase difficulty by changing the height of the ball and swinging it in a different path. The ball can travel in a circle, back and forth, side-to-side, etc. Remember, the athlete should never move his head, only his eyes.

The athlete can get his body involved by using his pointer finger to point at the ball while it's moving. His focus should still be on reading the letters and numbers on the ball. Have the athlete use his dominant hand first, then his nondominant hand. Next, the athlete can use the right foot to point and then the left foot.

Variations: As the athlete becomes proficient in this exercise, begin to incorporate the following variations to increase the level of difficulty. Begin at the top of the list, master a variation, and then move to the next level of difficulty.

- Have the athlete stand on a balance beam.
- Ask the athlete to bounce on a mini trampoline.
- Add visual noise by using a strobe light or strobe specs. (This variation should not be performed if the athlete suffers from seizures.)

**Beanbag Toss**
Group: EM
Objective: To straighten eye alignment as well as work on convergence, divergence, accommodation, and eye-hand-body

coordination

Equipment: A beanbag

Instructions: The trainer and athlete stand an appropriate distance apart according to the athlete's skill level. Begin tossing the beanbags back and forth underhanded in a game of catch, with the athlete's eyes following the path of the beanbag. (Again, the athlete should move only his or her eyes.) The trainer will change the path of his tosses during this exercise, but the athlete should be directed to toss the bag directly back to the trainer every time.

The trainer makes the throws easy to catch at first. Then, tosses are made to different areas to the left and right of the athlete to increase the level of difficulty. Also, the trainer mingles in occasional throws with high arcs, forcing the athlete to use upward gaze.

Variations: As the athlete becomes proficient in this exercise, begin to incorporate the following variations to increase the level of difficulty. Begin at the top of the list, master a variation, and move to the next level of difficulty.

- Have the athlete stand on one foot and alternate.
- Tell the athlete to run in place.
- Ask the athlete to jump up and down.
- Have the athlete bounce on a mini trampoline.
- Add visual noise by using strobe glasses or a strobe light flashing at the fastest level, then slow it down to increase difficulty. (This variation should not be performed if the athlete suffers from seizures.)

**Pirate Patch Beanbag Toss**

Group: EM

Objective:     To     improve     eye-muscle     movement     by concentrating on one eye

Equipment: Beanbags and a pirate patch or eye patch

Instructions: The trainer and athlete stand an appropriate distance apart according to the athlete's skill level. The athlete wears a pirate patch over his nondominant eye to start this exercise.

Begin tossing a beanbag back and forth underhanded in a game of catch, with the athlete's eyes following the path of the beanbag. The trainer will change the path of his tosses during this exercise, but the athlete should be directed to toss the bag directly back to the trainer. The trainer makes the throws easy to catch at first. Harder tosses off to the right and left sides and the occasional high arc are incorporated as soon as the athlete masters catching the beanbags that have come from straight-ahead throws. It may take a while for the athlete to become good at this task because he will have poor depth perception. This part of the exercise should be done for two minutes and should begin with easier tosses for straight-ahead catching.

Now, move the patch over to cover the dominant eye. This is where the fun really begins! The trainer repeats the straight-ahead tosses. It will take some time to move past straight-ahead throws and catches. Eventually the trainer can incorporate throws to the left and right side and the occasional high toss. This part of the exercise works the athlete's weaker eye and is probably the most important part of this drill. It should be performed for two minutes as well.

The last minute of this exercise is performed with the pirate patch off. The trainer throws the beanbag way off to the right and left sides (errant passes). As the beanbag is in the air, the trainer yells out the location where the athlete has to toss the beanbag after he catches it. This can be in any part of the room.

The athlete catches the beanbag where it was thrown and tosses it to the part of the room that the trainer specified. The goal of this part of the exercise is to move the athlete around for fitness, allow him to develop better spatial awareness, concentrate on throwing to a specific spot other than the trainer, and improve the accuracy of the athlete's throws.

Variations: As the athlete becomes proficient in this exercise, begin to incorporate the following variations to increase the level of difficulty. Begin at the top of the list, master that variation, and then move to the next level of difficulty.

- Have the athlete stand on one foot and alternate.
- Tell the athlete to run in place.
- Ask the athlete to jump up and down.
- Have the athlete bounce on a mini trampoline.
- Add visual noise by using strobe glasses or a strobe light flashing at the fastest level, then slow it down to increase the difficulty level. (This variation should not be performed if the athlete suffers from seizures.)

**Paper Towel Roll Exercise**

Group: EM

Objective: To decrease suppression or train the nondominant eye for aiming

Equipment: A cardboard paper towel roll and a television

Instructions: The athlete watches television while holding the paper towel roll up to her nondominant or suppressed eye. The athlete should see the tube circling around the television and some of the picture should be cut off. The athlete may have to close the dominant eye to get the brain to see the television through the paper towel roll. As the athlete gets better at ignoring the dominant eye, she will feel more at ease looking through the tube.

If the athlete has trouble ignoring her dominant eye, the athlete can begin this exercise by holding the paper towel roll up to the dominant eye and ignoring the image seen through the roll.

**Table Exercise**

Group: V

Objective: To improve convergence

Equipment: A table, painting or masking tape, three pieces from a game of Monopoly

This exercise requires a little setup. Make a three-foot straight line of tape on the table with the beginning of the line of tape at one edge of the table. Next, place the Monopoly pieces on the tape. (I'll use the thimble, dog, and hat as my game pieces.) Place the dog on the tape about six inches from the edge of the table. Place the hat in the middle of the line of tape. Place the thimble about three inches from the other end of the tape.

Instructions: The athlete stands or sits at the edge of the table so that her nose is directly over the beginning of the tape pointing toward our object. The trainer calls out one of the objects. The athlete looks at that object and continues to fixate on it. After a count of three, the trainer calls out a different object. The athlete switches her fixation to the new object. After another count of three, the trainer will call out another of the objects for the athlete to fixate on. Continue randomly changing and fixating on the three objects throughout the exercise period.

Variation: You can substitute Scrabble pieces. Using three *A* letters is best. Place them in the same positions on the tape so that they are upright and facing the athlete. The trainer instructs the athlete to look at either the front, middle, or back Scrabble piece. The athlete should concentrate on looking at the very top peak of each letter *A* throughout this exercise.

**Two Pennies Three**

Group: V

Objective: To improve convergence

Equipment: A table, two pennies

Instructions: Place two pennies an inch apart on a table with Abe Lincoln's picture facing up and in the same orientation. (You should be able to draw a straight line between the two noses on the pennies.) The athlete positions her head about 16 inches directly above the pennies so that her nose points to a spot directly in the middle of the space between them. The athlete then crosses her eyes in such a manner that the two pennies become three. She should concentrate on the penny in the middle and work to keep that image clear and together. She should hold this for a count of 10 and release. After resting for another count of 10, she should perform the task again. Have her do this for five repetitions.

Now move the pennies so that they are two inches apart and repeat.

Again, move the pennies so that they are three inches apart and repeat.

If the athlete cannot bring the pennies together into a single central image after the pennies are spread a certain distance apart, she should move the pennies back and work at the level where she could last bring it together.

Tip: If the athlete has trouble starting this exercise, she can hold a pencil so that the tip is about six inches above the pennies. Doing this can help her get a feel for crossing her eyes.

**Penny Christmas Tree**

Group: V

Objective: To improve convergence

Equipment: A table, 10 pennies

This exercise requires a little setup. On a table, make a penny pyramid or Christmas tree by using 10 pennies. At the top of the tree are two pennies placed an inch apart as in the Two Pennies Three exercise. The second branch should be an inch below the first branch and have two pennies that are two inches apart. The third penny branch should have two pennies that are three inches apart, one inch below the second branch. The fourth branch should have two pennies four inches apart and one inch below the third branch. The fifth branch should have two pennies five inches apart and one inch below the fourth.

Instructions: The athlete positions his head so that his nose is pointing in the middle of the third branch and about 16 inches above the tree. Now, the athlete crosses his eyes so that the two pennies on the first branch become three. The athlete should focus on the image of the penny that is in the middle. He should hold this for a count of 10, then rest for a count of 10. Next he should drop down to the next branch and make those two pennies one for another count of 10. The athlete continues to work all the way to the bottom branch of the tree, making the two pennies on each branch converge. Once he has held the pennies on the bottom branch as a single image for a count of 10, the athlete goes back up to the fourth branch and completes the same process but moving back up from the bottom to the top of the tree. This walking up and down the branches should be practiced for a total of five minutes.

This exercise is similar to the Two Pennies Three exercise except that the athlete has to jump from one convergence level to the other. Some athletes may get to the third or fourth branch and be unable to bring the pennies on the next branch down into one. The athlete should then focus on working down to the branch that he can make single and then back up from there. The goal is to be able to get all the way down to the bottom branch and then back up.

To increase the difficulty, the athlete can bring his nose closer to the tree, so that the pennies are about 12 inches away.

**Creep Up a String**

Group: V

Objective: To improve convergence

Equipment: Kite string, door with doorknob

This exercise requires a little setup. Tie a six- to nine-foot piece of kite string to a doorknob.

Instructions: The athlete sits six to nine feet from the door-knob and holds the untied end of the string to her nose so that the string is pulled taut. About one foot from the door, the trainer puts the entire length of his index finger along the string so that the tip is pointing to the athlete. The athlete concentrates on the tip of the trainer's finger as the trainer begins to move his finger closer to the athlete. The finger should go up to about half an inch from the athlete's nose and then slide back to the original starting spot. This should be repeated five times.

**Card Focus**

Group: F

Objective: To improve accommodation

Equipment: 20 note or index cards and a marker

This exercise requires a little setup. Number the note cards from 1 to 10 so that you have two of each number. (If the cards have lines on them, use the blank side on the back.) The numbers should be about an inch high and directly in the center of the card, and the card's orientation should be portrait rather than landscape: longer from top to bottom than from side to side. The trainer then gets one set of 10 cards and the athlete gets the other 10 cards. Each shuffles his or her cards so that the numbers are mixed.

Instructions: The athlete and trainer stand about 15 feet apart. The athlete holds her cards at about belly button level while the trainer holds his cards at chest level. The athlete starts by reading the top card in her deck, then looks up to read the top card in the trainer's deck. The athlete then reads the next card in her own deck, then looks back up to read the trainer's next card. Each of you turns up the next card in your decks as quickly as possible during this exercise and puts them back in the stack after the athlete reads them. The athlete continues this back-and-forth pattern of reading the cards until you've gone through the entire deck five times.

You can substitute playing cards, Uno cards, etc., for more variety.


**Peripheral Awareness**

Group: P

Objective: To improve object recognition in an athlete's extreme side vision

Equipment needed: 10 objects of different sizes in a box. (Examples: basketball, baseball, football, block, Matchbox car, pencil, tennis ball, stuffed animal, hockey puck, soccer ball, etc.)

Instructions: The athlete sits or stands about 10 feet from the $X$ on the wall and fixates his gaze on that spot throughout the exercise. The trainer stands behind the athlete. The trainer pulls an object out of the box and slowly brings it around to one side of the athlete's head at a distance of about three feet.

The goal is for the athlete to use his side vision to determine what object the trainer is holding. The trainer continues to move the object slowly into the athlete's field of view from the side until the athlete recognizes the object. Once the athlete has correctly identified the object the trainer puts it back in the box, selects another one, and starts the process again. This should be done for five minutes, and the trainer should switch sides so that left and right side vision are equally exercised.

Variations: As the athlete becomes proficient in this exercise, begin to incorporate the following variations to increase the level of difficulty. Begin at the top of the list, master that variation, and move to the next level of difficulty.

- Tell the athlete to run in place.
- Have the athlete jump in place.
- Ask the athlete to ride a stationary bike.
- Have the athlete bounce on a mini trampoline.
- Add visual noise by using a strobe light or strobe specs. (This variation should not be performed if the athlete suffers from seizures.)


**Eraser Board Circles and Squares**

Group: P

Objective: To improve peripheral awareness

Equipment: Dry-erase board and markers (or a chalkboard and chalk)

Instructions: The athlete stands in front of the dry-erase board or chalkboard with a marker or chalk (whichever is appropriate) in each hand. The athlete begins drawing a clockwise circle with his right hand that is at around 10 to 12 inches in diameter. The athlete continues to draw this circle over and over. After he has drawn the circle with the right hand, the athlete begins drawing a similar circle with his left hand, also 10 to 12 inches across and also in a clockwise rotation. Continue for about one minute. The trainer then tells the athlete to change the direction of the right hand to counterclockwise. After about 30 seconds, the athlete changes the rotation of the left hand to counterclockwise also. This continues for about one minute. Now, the trainer randomly directs the athlete to reverse the rotation of either the right or left hand. The trainer allows the athlete to get a good feel for the new direction, 30 seconds or so, and then instructs him to reverse the rotation of either one of the hands again.

Variations: As the athlete becomes proficient in this exercise, begin to incorporate the following variations to increase the level of difficulty. Begin at the top of the list, master that variation, and move to the next level of difficulty.

- Ask the athlete to draw squares or triangles instead of circles.
- Have the athlete stand on one leg.
- Tell the athlete to stand on a balance beam.

**Scrabble Piece Side-Vision Game**
  Group: P
  Objective: To expand peripheral awareness
  Equipment: 10 to 15 Scrabble letters
  This exercise requires a little setup. Place 10 to 15 Scrabble letters face up on the floor or on a table, spread out over an area of four feet by four feet. Place the letter *A* in the center and orient all of the letters in reading position for the athlete, who

stands or sits with her eyes approximately 16 to 24 inches above the letters and fixated on the middle letter *A*.

Instructions: The athlete concentrates on the letter *A* at the center of the table and does not move her eyes or her head. The trainer then points to different letters throughout the exercise area while the athlete uses her side vision to determine what letter the trainer is pointing out.

Variations: As the athlete becomes proficient in this exercise, begin to incorporate the following variations to increase the level of difficulty. Begin at the top of the list, master that variation, and move to the next level of difficulty.

- Ask the athlete to stand on one foot.
- Tell the athlete to run in place.
- Have the athlete jump in place.
- Add visual noise by using a strobe light or strobe specs. (This variation should not be performed if the athlete suffers from seizures.)

**Bounce a Ball and Catch**

Group: F and EH

Objective: To improve eye-muscle movement, convergence, accommodation, and eye-hand-body coordination

Equipment: A tennis ball and permanent marker

This exercise requires a little setup. Write the numbers *1*, *2*, and *3* on a tennis ball with a permanent black marker. The numbers should be about one and a half inches high and spaced to be an equal distance from each other.

Instructions: The trainer stands about 10 to 15 feet from the athlete and tosses the ball so that it bounces on the ground once before the athlete catches it.

The athlete focuses on the ball throughout its entire journey and yells out the last number she sees as the ball touches her hand.

Variations: As the athlete becomes proficient in this exercise, begin to incorporate the following variations to increase the level of difficulty. Begin at the top of the list, master that variation, and move to the next level of difficulty.

- Have the athlete wear a pirate patch to exercise one eye at a time.
- Ask the athlete to stand on a bed.
- Tell the athlete to bounce on a mini trampoline.

**Bounce a Ball and Turn Around**

Group: EH

Objective: To improve eye-hand-body coordination

Equipment: Beach ball or large bouncy ball

Instructions: Athlete and trainer stand about 15 feet apart facing each other. The trainer bounces the ball toward the athlete in such a manner that it will bounce about 10 feet in the air. When the trainer throws the ball, the athlete performs a complete spin with her body and then tries to find the ball and catch it as it comes down from the bounce.

**Bounce a Ball and Hit with a Stick**

Group: EH

Objective: To improve eye-hand-body coordination

Equipment: Beach ball, cardboard paper towel roll

This exercise requires a little setup. On the roll, color a one-inch band around one end with a black permanent marker, on the other end color a one-inch red band, and in the middle color a one-inch blue band.

Instructions: The athlete sits or stands, holding the roll

parallel to the ground with her hands on the uncolored parts of the cardboard. The trainer bounces the ball toward the athlete. As the ball is approaching, the trainer randomly calls out a color for the athlete to use to bunt or hit the ball as it approaches.

If a bouncing ball is too difficult, have the athlete sit on the floor and roll the ball to the athlete.

If a paper towel roll is too difficult, you can use a Pringles potato chip can. Use masking tape to create the three one-inch bands around the can and then color those in with the corresponding colors.

You can add visual noise to this exercise by using a strobe light or strobe glasses. (This should not be performed if the athlete suffers from seizures.)

**Juggling**

Group: EH

Objective: To improve eye-hand-body coordination

Equipment: Two beanbags

Instructions: The athlete learns to juggle by holding two beanbags, one in each hand. The right hand usually begins by throwing the beanbag underhanded in a slow arc so that it rises to a spot about six inches above the left hand and then drops down into that hand. While the first beanbag is traveling through the air, the left hand throws its beanbag straight over into the right hand. The athlete continues this motion, shifting the bags from hand to hand in a counterclockwise circle, throughout the training session.

There are several sites on the Internet that provide instructions for learning how to juggle. This is a hard skill to learn, so for those at a young age, just start with two beanbags or even just one bag. Feel free to add a third bag when desired.

Variations: As the athlete becomes proficient in this exercise, begin to incorporate the following variations to increase the level of difficulty. Begin at the top of the list, master that variation, and move to the next level of difficulty.

• Ask the athlete to stand on a balance beam.
• Ask the athlete to stand on one leg.

**Soccer Ball/Hacky Sack Juggle**

Group: EH

Objective: To improve eye-hand-body coordination

Equipment: Soccer ball or hacky sack

Instructions: The athlete stands in place and balances the soccer ball/hacky sack on top of the right foot, then kicks it up into the air so that it rises about two feet and then drops down toward the left foot. The athlete then uses the left foot to kick the soccer ball/hacky sack back over to the right foot. The athlete continues this pattern for the training session.

There are several sites on the Internet that athletes can use to learn how to juggle with their feet. This exercise is also a great way to increase core body temperature before competition.

**Two-Card Remember**

Group: ME

Objective: To help improve visual memory and peripheral awareness

Equipment: A table, a deck of playing cards

Instructions: The trainer divides the deck of cards into two piles and places them face down on a table. The trainer sits on one side of the table and the athlete sits on the other. The trainer flips up two cards and shows them to the athlete, then turns the cards quickly away. The athlete then tells the trainer what the two cards were.

Variations: As the athlete becomes proficient in this exercise, begin to incorporate the following variations to increase the level of difficulty. Begin at the top of the list, master that variation, and move to the next level of difficulty.

- Add visual noise by using a strobe light or strobe glasses. (This variation should not be performed if the athlete suffers from seizures.)
- Yell and scream at the moment the athlete views the cards.
- Another trainer can lightly shake or jostle the athlete as he or she views the cards (perturbation).

### Three/Four-Card Game

Group: ME

Objective: To improve visual memory

Equipment: A deck of playing cards, a swivel chair, a table

The athlete sits in a chair that rotates and faces away from the table. The trainer places three (or four) cards in a line face up on the table. The athlete revolves to see the cards and then a moment later revolves away. The athlete then tells the trainer what cards were showing.

There are a couple of variations you can use if you don't have a swivel chair. The trainer can hold his hands over the athlete's eyes and perform the exercise like a simple game of peek-a-boo. The trainer can also hold a book a couple of inches over the cards so that they are hidden, remove the book so the cards are visible, and then quickly cover the cards back up.

Variations: As the athlete becomes proficient in this exercise, begin to incorporate the following variations to increase the level of difficulty. Begin at the top of the list, master a variation, and then move to the next level of difficulty.

- Add visual noise by using a strobe light or strobe glasses. (This variation should not be performed if the athlete suffers from seizures.)
- Yell and scream at the moment the athlete views the cards.

**Monopoly Piece Memory Game**

Group: ME

Objective: To improve visual memory

Equipment: Pieces from a Monopoly game, a table

Instructions: This exercise is similar to the Three/Four-Card Game above, only you substitute Monopoly game pieces for the cards. The trainer arranges three game pieces in a line and covers the pieces from view. The trainer lifts up his hand to reveal the pieces and quickly covers them back up. The athlete tells the trainer what the pieces were in order from left to right; for example: hat, thimble, race car. The trainer adjusts the pieces to a different order, and the exercise starts again. This exercise should be performed for five minutes, and pieces can be added or substituted from time to time.

Variations: As the athlete becomes proficient in this exercise, begin to incorporate the following variations to increase the level of difficulty. Begin at the top of the list, master that variation, and move to the next level of difficulty.

- Add visual noise by using a strobe light or strobe glasses. (This variation should not be performed if the athlete suffers from seizures.)
- Yell and scream at the moment the athlete views the cards.

**Scrabble Piece Memory Game**

Group: ME

Objective: To improve visual memory

Equipment: 30 Scrabble pieces

Instructions: The trainer sets up 10 different stations with three Scrabble letters each, similar to the Monopoly Piece Memory Game above. Note cards are placed over each station to hide the letters. The athlete is shown the letters at the first station for a second and then repeats from memory the letters in order. The athlete then moves on to the next station to continue the game.

Variations: As the athlete becomes proficient in this exercise, begin to incorporate the following variations to increase the level of difficulty. Begin at the top of the list, master that variation, and move to the next level of difficulty.

- Set up stations with four letters and then move up to five letters.
- Add visual noise by using a strobe light or strobe glasses. (This variation should not be performed if the athlete suffers from seizures.)
- Yell and scream at the moment the athlete views the cards.

# CHAPTER 12
## SEE TO PLAY VISION EXERCISES

This chapter is designed to give athletes tools to optimize their visual systems so that they can perform to their genetic potentials. These exercises build on the work described in the previous chapter, which may also contain exercises that you'll find useful. By performing the exercises found in these chapters, athletes develop better visual skills in order to see to play. The areas of the visual system that are targeted for training include eye muscles, eye teaming, eye focusing, peripheral awareness, eye-hand-body coordination, and the mind's eye.

You'll notice that these exercises are free-space exercises. Athletes can do many of these exercises alone, without the assistance of a trainer or partner. They can be done at home or on the road. There are variations given along with the drills to increase the level of difficulty and provide variety. As in the previous chapter, I've made the training equipment easy to access and inexpensive, often derived from items found around your home. I have also included some exercises that use equipment that you cannot make but that is available from an eye doctor's office or through my website (www.seetoplay.com).

I have assigned each exercise to a group. The groups are:

EM: Eye-Muscle Movement
V: Vergence (Convergence and Divergence)
F: Focusing

PD: **P**eripheral Awareness, **D**etailed Vision Zone
PS: **P**eripheral Awareness, Extreme **S**ide Vision
EH: **E**ye-**H**and-Body Coordination
ME: **M**ind's **E**ye

### Practice Schedule

I recommend that athletes perform these exercises at the same time every weekday (such as 9:00–9:25 pm) so that this becomes a daily routine. I also recommend that they train their eyes for a period of nine weeks and then take a three-week break.

The daily schedule can vary as follows:

Monday-Wednesday-Friday
• 5 minutes of one exercise from group EM
• 5 minutes of one exercise from group V
• 5 minutes of one exercise from group F
• 10 minutes of one exercise from group EH

Tuesday-Thursday
• 5 minutes of one exercise from group PD
• 5 minutes of one exercise from group PS
• 15 minutes of one exercise from group ME

Use the chart below as a menu to design your daily and weekly workouts. Try to use each of the exercises before you start to repeat them. The exercises are explained in full throughout the rest of the chapter.

## Exercise Menu

|                                      | EM | V | F | PD | PS | EH | ME |
|--------------------------------------|----|---|---|----|----|----|----|
| Eye-Muscle Movement Drill            | X  |   |   |    |    |    |    |
| Calendar Jump                        | X  |   |   |    |    |    |    |
| Paper Towel Roll                     | X  |   |   |    |    |    |    |
| Red/Green Brock String               | X  |   |   |    |    |    |    |
| Pencil Push-Up                       |    | X |   |    |    |    |    |
| Hot Dog Drill                        |    | X |   |    |    |    |    |
| Two Pennies Three                    |    | X |   |    |    |    |    |
| Penny Christmas Tree                 |    | X |   |    |    |    |    |
| Brock String                         |    | X |   |    |    |    |    |
| Deck-of-Cards Focus                  |    |   | X |    |    |    |    |
| Book/Calendar Scan                   |    |   | X |    |    |    |    |
| Card Toss                            |    |   | X |    |    |    |    |
| +/- Flippers                         |    |   | X |    |    |    |    |
| Detailed Vision Read                 |    |   |   | X  |    |    |    |
| Scrabble Pieces Read                 |    |   |   | X  |    |    |    |
| Chart Read                           |    |   |   | X  |    |    |    |
| Side-Vision Card Read                |    |   |   |    | X  |    |    |
| Side-Vision Swing                    |    |   |   |    | X  |    |    |
| Peripheral-Awareness Drill on a Bike |    |   |   |    | X  |    |    |
| Artwork Game                         |    |   |   |    | X  |    |    |
| Ball/Bunt                            |    |   |   |    |    | X  |    |
| Small Bat and Ball                   |    |   |   |    |    | X  |    |
| Ball Toss                            |    |   |   |    |    | X  |    |
| Juggling Drill                       |    |   |   |    |    | X  |    |
| Soccer Ball/Hacky Sack Juggle        |    |   |   |    |    | X  |    |
| Four/Seven-Card Game                 |    |   |   |    |    |    | X  |
| Scrabble Pieces Memory Game          |    |   |   |    |    |    | X  |
| Visualization                        |    |   |   |    |    |    | X  |
| Relaxation                           |    |   |   |    |    |    | X  |

## Log Sheets

Use the following charts as log sheets for your weekly exercises. Before you begin Monday's exercises, fill out the sheet completely with all the exercises you intend to perform. Make sure you try to incorporate all the different exercises before you start to repeat them. Also, check off the exercises after you have finished so that you have a good record of all the exercises you have performed. (I will also make log sheets available to download from my website www.seetoplay.com.)

|  | Monday | Tuesday | Wednesday | Thursday | Friday |
|---|---|---|---|---|---|
| **EM** 5 minutes |  | n/a |  | n/a |  |
| **V** 5 minutes |  | n/a |  | n/a |  |
| **F** 5 minutes |  | n/a |  | n/a |  |
| **EH** 10 minutes |  | n/a |  | n/a |  |
| **PD** 5 minutes | n/a |  | n/a |  | n/a |
| **PS** 5 minutes | n/a |  | n/a |  | n/a |
| **ME** 15 minutes | n/a |  | n/a |  | n/a |

## Exercises

### Eye-Muscle Movement Drill

Group: EM

Objective: To improve fine motor movement of the eye muscles

Equipment: None

Instructions: The athlete looks at a wall 10 feet away. He begins to move his eyes in a large zigzag pattern starting at the top left corner near the ceiling, tracing the top edge of the wall all the way to the right corner in a straight line and then diagonally back to the left edge of the wall about two feet below the beginning spot. The athlete traces an imaginary straight line back to the right edge of the wall and repeats the zigzag to another spot on the left edge of the wall two feet below the last starting spot. The athlete continues this exercise until he hits the bottom right corner where the wall and floor meet. Then he reverses the pattern and moves back up to the top. This warm-up lasts 30 seconds to one minute.

The next step is for the athlete to move his eyes in circular patterns. The athlete starts at a spot that represents twelve o'clock on the wall. He slowly moves his eyes full circle clockwise three times, stopping at twelve o'clock for a brief moment on each circle. The athlete then starts at the six o'clock spot and does three clockwise rotations. Afterward, the athlete starts back at twelve o'clock and completes three counterclockwise rotations with brief stops at the beginning spot. This is followed by three counterclockwise rotations that start at six o'clock.

Last, the athlete performs large figure-eight patterns of motion with the eyes by tracing an imaginary *8* on the wall. The athlete should perform two figure eights in one direction and then reverse the motion to the other direction.

**Calendar Jump**

Group: EM

Objective: To improve eye movement and eye scanning

Equipment: Two calendars of the same size

There is a little setup required. Place the two calendars at the same height on a wall at eye level to the athlete and so that they are four feet from each other. Each calendar should show a different month.

Instructions: The athlete stands 10 to 15 feet away from the wall and fixes her gaze on the first day of the month on the calendar on the left. She then shifts her gaze to the first day of the month on the calendar on the right, then moves to the second day on the calendar on the left, followed by the second day on the calendar on the right. She continues this back-and-forth movement all the way through all of the dates on the calendars and then starts back at the beginning.

Variations: As the athlete becomes proficient in the above exercise, begin to incorporate these variations to increase the level of difficulty. Begin at the top of the list, master that variation, and move to the next level of difficulty.

• Move the charts further apart to five feet and eventually to about eight feet from each other.

- Have the athlete bounce on a mini trampoline.
- Use different-sized calendars, with one considerably smaller than the other.

### Paper Towel Roll

Group: EM

Objective: To decrease suppression of a weak eye or to train the nondominant eye for aiming purposes

Equipment: A cardboard paper towel roll

Instructions: While watching television, the athlete holds the paper towel roll up to the nondominant or ignored eye. He concentrates on the image of the television that is circled by the paper towel roll. He then switches eyes and tries to ignore the image seen through the paper towel roll. Sometimes it is necessary for the athlete to close the eye he is trying to ignore. The goal is to concentrate on the weaker eye.

### Red/Green Brock String

Group: EM

Objective: To improve eye alignment and eye teaming

Equipment: Red/green glasses and a Brock string (both are available at an eye doctor's office or on my website). A Brock string has three beads on it. You can make your own string by using quarter-inch bolts tied on a six-to-nine-foot section of kite string, with the first bolt tied at the one-foot mark, the second bolt tied at the three-foot mark, and the last bolt tied at the five-foot mark.

There is a little setup required. Attach one end of the Brock string to a doorknob. The athlete puts the red/green glasses on and sits six to nine feet away so that the string is pulled taut and the end closest to the athlete is touching the tip of her nose. The bead that is nearest to the door should be about one foot away from the doorknob. The middle bead should be in the middle of the string, and the bead nearest the athlete should be one foot away from her nose.

Instructions: (I will describe this exercise as if you are using the Brock string and not the homemade string.) The athlete looks at the hole in the bead in the middle. While looking at that hole, the athlete will see a green string and a red string crossing at the bead, in front of the bead, or just after the bead.

If the athlete cannot see either the red or green string, she should alternately close each eye until she does see the string that was missing (due to one eye being suppressed). She then slowly opens the other eye while concentrating on the string that was originally not seen to train the brain to turn on the suppressed eye.

The athlete then switches her gaze to the near bead and determines if she sees both of the colored strings and the spot in space where they cross. She holds this gaze for a count of five and then moves her gaze to the final bead, where she repeats the task of looking for both colored strings as well as the spot where they cross in space. She holds her gaze and then moves on to another bead. The athlete repeats changing her gaze randomly to different beads throughout the exercise.

During the last 30 seconds of this exercise, the athlete shifts her gaze back to the middle bead. She again concentrates on where the colored strings cross in space. If this spot is in front of or behind the hole of the middle bead, she should try to concentrate so that the crossing point moves toward the hole of the bead. This may take some time to achieve but can be accomplished.

**Pencil Push-Up**

    Group: V

    Objective: To improve convergence

    Equipment: A pen or pencil

    Instructions: In this exercise, the fixation spot for the eyes is the tip of a pen or pencil. The athlete holds the tip at arm's length, with the pencil parallel to the ground and straight in front of his nose. He slowly brings the pencil toward the nose until it either touches the nose or the pencil tip appears to break into two. If it breaks into two, indicating that the athlete is seeing double, he moves it back to a spot that is one inch away and sees if he can make the images one again. Then the athlete moves the pencil completely back out. The goal is to bring the pencil tip completely in toward the nose without the image breaking into two. Continue bringing it in and out, parallel to the ground, for one minute. (The athlete can also substitute a finger if he does not have a pencil and would like to work on this exercise. If a finger is used, the athlete needs to pick one specific spot to concentrate on, such as the left corner of the fingernail on the right index finger or the top right corner of the fingernail of the left index finger.)

    The next phase of this exercise works the eyes from downward gaze. This is achieved by having the athlete drop the pencil (or finger) down about two and a half feet and begin the push-up movement of the object in toward the nose until the object turns into two or touches the nose. It is important that the athlete does not dip his chin but keeps his face and nose pointing straight ahead. This part of the exercise should last about one minute.

    The athlete next moves to the third part of this drill, which is working the eyes from upward gaze. This is achieved by holding the pencil about two feet above his head and bringing it down toward the nose until it either doubles or touches the nose. Then the athlete moves the pencil back out in a push-up manner. Again, the athlete should keep his chin and nose pointing straight ahead.

The athlete can then spend the remaining time of this exercise working on the area of gaze that was the most difficult for him and repeat the drill for that gaze again.

- An athlete who has an A-pattern weakness (see Chapter 4) should work more on the push-up coming in from the downward gaze.
- An athlete with a V-pattern weakness should work more on the push-up coming in from the top.

Variation: From time to time, the athlete can look at the pencil as he brings it toward him until it is about two inches from the nose. The athlete should stop moving the pencil at that point and look away from the pencil to an object that is a far distance across the room, focus on that object for three seconds, and then shift focus back to the pencil for three seconds. The athlete should repeat this back-and-forth motion for 30 seconds before returning to the normal Pencil Push-Up exercise.

**Hot Dog Drill**
Group: V
Objective: To improve convergence
Equipment: Two index fingers
Instructions: The athlete makes fists with both hands and holds them about 16 inches from his or her face. Next, the athlete straightens out both index or pointer fingers so that they are pointing at each other, forming a straight line. Then she brings

the fingertips in so that there is about a half-inch gap between the two fingers. By crossing her eyes, the right finger will appear to overlap the left finger and the athlete should see three fingers in all: a finger to the right, a finger to the left, and then a middle area where the two fingers overlap so that they have the appearance of a floating hot dog. The athlete concentrates on the floating hot dog and continues to keep it together as she slowly moves her fingers further apart from each other and then back closer together again. She should continue to try to bring the fingers farther and farther apart while keeping the hot dog floating. Then she should slowly bring the fingers back in to relieve the tension on the eyes.

**Two Pennies Three**

Group: V

Objective: To improve convergence

Equipment: Two pennies

Instructions: Place two pennies an inch apart on a table with Abe Lincoln's picture facing upright and in the same orientation. (The pennies should be placed in a manner such that the two points of the tips of Abraham Lincoln's nose form a straight line.) The athlete positions his or her head directly above the pennies so that his nose points to a spot directly in the middle of the space between the pennies and about 16 inches above the pennies. The athlete crosses his eyes in such a manner that the two pennies become three. The athlete concentrates on the penny in the middle, holds this for a count of 10, and releases. After a count of 10, he should perform the task again. The athlete should do this for five repetitions.

Now move the pennies two inches apart and repeat.

Again, move the pennies so that they are three inches apart

and repeat.

The athlete will get to the point where he cannot bring the pennies together after they are spread to a certain point. The athlete then starts at the level where he could last bring them together.

**Penny Christmas Tree**

Group: V

Objective: To improve convergence

Equipment: 10 pennies

Make a penny triangle or Christmas tree using 10 pennies. The top of the tree is two pennies placed an inch apart as in the exercise Two Pennies Three. The second branch should have two pennies that are two inches apart and an inch below the first branch. The third penny branch should have two pennies three inches apart and one inch below the second branch. The fourth branch should have two pennies four inches apart and one inch below the third branch. The fifth branch should have two pennies five inches apart and one inch below the fourth.

The athlete positions her head so that her nose is pointing in the middle of the third branch of the tree and about 16 inches above the tree. The athlete crosses her eyes in a manner that the two pennies in the first branch become three. The athlete concentrates on the penny in the middle, holds this for a count of 10, and drops down to the next row and makes those two pennies three, concentrating on the middle one for another count of 10. The athlete continues to move her gaze all the way to the bottom branch of the tree. Once the bottom branch's pennies have been worked for a count of 10, the athlete goes back up to the fourth row and completes the same process but this time walks her eyes back to the top of the tree. This walking up and down the branches should be performed for a total of five minutes.

The exercise is the similar to the Two Pennies Three exercise but also allows the athlete to work on different levels of convergence. Some athletes may get to the third or fourth branch and be unable to bring the pennies on the next branch together into one. Those athletes should focus on working up and down from the branch that they successfully made single. The goal is to be able to get all the way down to the bottom branch and then back up.

For added difficulty, the athlete can adjust her nose so that it is about 12 inches from the tree.

**Brock String**

Group: V

Objective: To improve convergence and eye alignment

Equipment: A training partner and a Brock string, which is available on my website or may be available at your eye doctor's office. You can also make your own string as described above for the Red/Green Brock String exercise.

Instructions: The athlete and a training partner stand at a distance holding either end of the string so that it is completely stretched out. The end beads on the string should be about two feet from each end, and the middle bead should be in the center. The athlete takes the string and places the end at the tip of his nose. The trainer keeps the string at the athlete's eye level. The athlete focuses on the middle bead. He should notice that he sees two beads at the end of the string near the trainer and two beads near his own end. While looking at the middle bead, he should pay attention to the two strings that are leaving from the beads at both ends. The strings should cross at the middle bead or just a little in front or back of it. If the strings cross a good bit in front of or behind the middle bead, the athlete should try to make the strings cross at the middle of the bead by overfocusing his eyes.

If the athlete only sees one string and three beads total, this means that he is suppressing or ignoring one eye. The athlete should stop this exercise and do the Red/Green Brock String exercise or the Paper Towel Roll exercise found above instead.

Once the athlete has the strings crossing at the middle bead, it is time to start jumping the gaze from bead to bead. The trainer calls out the color or position of a bead, and the athlete shifts focus to that bead. The athlete needs to be sure that he is still seeing two beads and two strings leading away from the middles of each bead that he focuses on. He should jump back and forth between the three different beads for a five-minute period.

The next step is to perform this in the other eight areas of primary gaze. The trainer holds her end of the string up or down and from side to side to those other areas to achieve this goal. The other areas of gaze are: above right, above central, above left, right of straight ahead, left of straight ahead, below right, below central, and below left.

Variations: To increase difficulty, the athlete can perform this exercise while standing on a balance board or mini trampoline.

**Deck-of-Cards Focus**

Group: F

Objective: To improve accommodation

Equipment: A deck of playing cards, a calendar on a wall

Instructions: The athlete holds a deck of playing cards face down while sitting about 15 feet away from a calendar. (Alternatively, the athlete can make the distance target a television turned to a station that has continually scrolling information across the bottom, such as ESPN, a financial channel, or a news channel.)

The athlete holds the cards about 10 inches from her face and at a level even with her belly button. The athlete flips the first card over, focuses on the writing to determine which card it is, and then discards the card while looking up to focus on the date at the bottom right of the calendar (or the lettering on the TV; this scrolling text on the screen adds difficulty). Next, the athlete shifts her focus back to the deck and lifts up another card to repeat the sequence: read, discard, and focus on the previous date on the calendar (reading the numbers backward, such as 30, 29, 28, etc.). The athlete continues this process until all of the cards are gone, moving as quickly as possible but taking care to see the letters clearly, not just skim over them, before moving to the next step.

Variation: Use a pirate patch over one eye to exercise each eye separately.

### Book/Calendar Scan

Group: F

Objective: To improve accommodation

Equipment: A book, a calendar on a wall

Instructions: Place a calendar on a wall. The athlete sits in a chair 10 to 15 feet away with a book in his hands. The athlete reads a line from a page of the book, then looks up and reads a line from the calendar. He continues scanning back and forth throughout the exercise period.

Variation: Use a pirate patch over one eye to exercise each eye separately. This is important to do if the athlete is ignoring one eye. Patch the stronger eye to help the brain learn to use the weaker eye.

**Card Toss**

Group: F

Objective: To improve accommodation

Equipment: Several decks of playing cards, a training partner

Instructions: The athlete and a training partner sit facing each other about 10 to 15 feet apart. Each of them holds a deck of cards face down. The trainer says, "Start," and the athlete lifts up his first card, reads it aloud, discards it to the floor, and then reads the card that the trainer has brought up from the top of her own deck. The athlete shifts focus to his own deck, pulls up the top card, reads it, discards it, and looks up to read the next card from the trainer's deck.

The athlete continues to read cards using this back-and-forth motion until all of the cards from the decks have been used. The athlete's visual system actually gets a break from the workout while the cards are being picked up. To lengthen the workout, the athlete and trainer should use four to five decks apiece. These decks should be kept directly to the side of both the trainer and athlete for easy retrieval. (You'll end up with a huge pile of mixed-up cards but the workout is worth it!)

Variations:

- Have your athlete wear a pirate patch to concentrate on the weaker performing eye.
- Use a stopwatch to time how many cards a player can read per minute. Try to increase the number of cards read each minute.
- Have your athlete bounce on a mini trampoline.

**+/- Flippers**

Group: F

Objective: To improve accommodation

Equipment: +/- 1.50 D flippers, a book (The flippers can be purchased at your eye doctor's office or at www.seetoplay.com.)

Instructions: The athlete sits in a chair at a desk with the book (or other reading material) at a comfortable distance. The athlete then wears the +/- 1.50 flippers to read through. The athlete reads through one side of the lenses for 10 seconds and then flips the lenses over and reads through the other side for 10 seconds.

Variations: As the athlete becomes proficient in the above exercise, begin to incorporate these variations to increase the level of difficulty. Begin at the top of the list, master that variation, and move to the next level of difficulty.

- Move up to +/- 2.50 D flippers.
- Use red/green glasses instead of the flippers and place a red/green trainer (a sheet of plastic with red and green stripes on it) over the reading material. (This equipment is also available on my website or at an eye doctor's office.)
- Add visual noise by reading while a strobe light is flashing. (This variation should not be performed if the athlete suffers from seizures.)

**Detailed Vision Read**

Group: PD

Objective: To optimize peripheral awareness in the athlete's detailed vision zone

Equipment: A deck of playing cards

Instructions: The athlete places a deck of playing cards in her right hand facing in, so that the lettering is visible. She finds a fixation spot with straight-ahead gaze and continues to stare at it throughout this exercise. The athlete extends her arm out fully and moves the cards to the right so that the arm forms about a 45-degree angle to the straight-ahead gaze. The arm remains extended throughout the exercise and does not bend. Next, the athlete slowly brings her arm in toward the midline, just until she can determine the number or letter at the top left corner of the card. The athlete continues to bring the card into full view without diverting her gaze from the fixation spot to determine if she read the card correctly. Once she has determined that she read the card correctly, she moves the pack down out of view, discards the card that was just read so that a new card is ready, and moves her arm back out to the 45-degree-angle position. The athlete repeats the process again with a new card and continues this drill for two minutes.

The athlete repeats the exercise from the left side. The deck of cards is held in the left hand and the arm comes in from the left side from the 45-degree-angle starting point. When exercising the outside edge of the zone in the left eye, the athlete reads the numbers or letters at the bottom right of the card.

Variations: As the athlete becomes proficient in this exercise, begin to incorporate these variations to increase the level of difficulty. Begin at the top of the list, master that variation, and move to the next level of difficulty.

- Ask your athlete to stand on a balance board.
- Have your athlete ride a stationary bike and become fatigued.
- Add visual noise by using strobe glasses or a strobe light. (This variation should not be performed if the athlete suffers from seizures.)

**Scrabble Pieces Read**

Group: PD

Objective: To improve peripheral awareness

Equipment: 30 Scrabble pieces, a training partner

There is a little setup required. Make 10 stations with three Scrabble letters each, spread out over an area of four feet by six feet on a table or the floor. The stations should be equal distances apart.

Instructions: The athlete sits or stands about three feet from the reading surface and concentrates on the station of letters in the center. The athlete does not move his eyes from this station for the entire exercise. Now, a training partner points to different letters throughout the different stations, and the athlete uses his side vision to determine what the letters are at that station and tells them to the trainer. (The athlete can perform this exercise alone as well.)

**Chart Read**

Group: PD

Objective: To improve peripheral awareness in the detailed vision zone

Equipment: The "DVZ Improver" chart. I have included a sample of this chart, which I made using my computer, on the last page of this chapter. You can also download a PDF version of this chart from my website at www.seetoplay.com.

Instructions: The athlete tapes the chart to a wall or places it on a table that he or she can lean over. The athlete positions herself directly in front of (or above) the dot in the center, about 16 inches away. Without moving her eyes, she starts finding the letters of the alphabet in order. If she has trouble finding a letter, she can move on to the next letter after about five seconds of trying. After completing this task, the athlete can find the letters in reverse alphabetical order.

Variations for the athlete to try: Keep one eye closed.

• Ride on a stationary bike.

**Side-Vision Card Read**

Group: PS

Objective: To improve peripheral awareness in the extreme side-vision zone

Equipment: Two playing cards

Instructions: The athlete holds his right arm straight out to his right side so that the card is even with his right ear. Next, he moves the card further back so that it goes behind his range of view. While concentrating on a fixation spot straight ahead, the athlete slowly brings the card into view until he notices just the outer edge of the card (he will not be able to read the letter or number on the card but should be able to see the outer edge of the card in general). He can shake the card to make it easier to see if he has problems at first. The athlete should repeat five to 10 times and then move to the left side. He should continue alternating the exercise on the right and left sides.

**Side-Vision Swing**

Group: PS

Objective: To improve peripheral awareness in the extreme side-vision zone

Equipment: Two playing cards

Instructions: The athlete holds one card in each hand with the number or letter facing in and holds both arms straight out to the sides so that her body forms a *T*. Next she moves both cards back further until they are out of view of both eyes. While concentrating on a fixation spot straight ahead, she brings the right card in until she can see it. Next, she moves it back out of view while simultaneously bringing the left card forward until she sees it. Again, she moves the left arm back until that card is out of view while bringing the right card into view. The athlete continues this back-and-forth swinging motion for five minutes.

### Peripheral-Awareness Drill on a Bike

Group: PS

Objective: To improve peripheral awareness

Equipment: Stationary bike or treadmill

Instructions: When the athlete is on a stationary bike or treadmill, he or she fixates on the TV or another object straight ahead and then works on identifying details of other objects that are in the room.

Examples: Try to count the people in a picture that is hanging off to one side. Try to determine what color clothing different people in the room are wearing. Try to determine what's playing on another television and then catalog each of the other objects in the room, starting close to the TV and moving further out.

Variation: While on a practice field and focusing on the task at hand, athletes can also try paying attention to all of the details around them, such as identifying teammates, the advertising shown, etc.

### Artwork Game

Group: PS

Objective: To increase peripheral awareness in both the detailed vision zone and the extreme vision zone

Equipment: Artwork hanging on a wall in a hotel or at home

Instructions: The athlete stands about 16 inches away from a picture and gazes at one spot in the middle. Next, he picks out all of the details that he can by using his peripheral vision only.

## Ball/Bunt

Group: EH

Objective: To improve eye-hand coordination

Equipment: A training partner, a two-foot piece of a dowel rod, and a Marsden ball, which can be purchased at an eye doctor's office or on my website.

You can make your own equipment by sawing off a two-foot section of a broom handle and sanding down the rough end and by inserting an eyelet screw into a hard plastic baseball or softball, similar to a Wiffle ball, and tying a 15-foot piece of kite string to the screw.

This requires a little setup. The ball should be suspended from the ceiling in such a manner that its height will be easily adjustable. When the exercise begins, the hanging ball should be at chest level to the athlete.

Place three different-colored stripes of tape on the two-foot dowel rod. A stripe should be placed two inches inside each end of the rod and then directly in the center of the rod. For example, you could put a red stripe at one end, a blue stripe at the other end, and a black stripe in the middle.

Instructions: The athlete holds the dowel with his or her hands on the wood on either side of the middle stripe of tape. The trainer starts the exercise by swinging the ball toward the athlete. As the ball gets close to the athlete, the trainer calls out the color of one of the stripes. The athlete bunts the ball with the part of the dowel that has the corresponding tape color. The trainer continues to call out different colors and the athlete continues to bunt the ball according to these directions.

Variations: As the athlete becomes proficient in the above exercise, begin to incorporate these variations to increase the level of difficulty. Begin at the top of the list, master that variation, and move to the next level of difficulty.

- Use a pirate patch over one eye. Exercise each eye separately.
- Vary the height of the ball.
- Have your athlete bounce on a mini trampoline.
- Use strobe glasses or a strobe light. (This variation should not be performed if the athlete suffers from seizures.)

**Small Bat and Ball**

Group: EH

Objective: To improve eye-hand coordination

Equipment: A training partner, a three-foot piece of a dowel rod, Wiffle golf balls

You can make your own equipment by sawing off a three-foot section of a broom handle and sanding down the rough end.

Instructions: The training partner stands about 15 feet from the athlete. The trainer pitches a golf ball underhanded toward the athlete, who tries to hit the ball as in a baseball or softball game. Faster pitches and overhand pitches can be added to increase difficulty.

**Ball Toss**

Group: EH

Objectives: This exercise is used to:

- Increase concentration/focus
- Increase eye-hand-body coordination
- Increase peripheral awareness
- Increase flexibility of the shoulder and pelvic girdle while maintaining good core strength

- Increase active range of motion
- Improve reaction time to weaker quadrants
- Improve mental anticipation and projection
- Stabilize and maintain a forward-facing position
- Increase core temperature for actual competition

Equipment: A neon-green tennis ball, an athletic training partner

Instructions: This exercise uses throws that increase in intensity, so it is important that both participants prepare their throwing arms through proper stretching and warm-up. One aim of this exercise is to stretch many of the muscle groups that the athlete uses in competition, but specifically stretching the thigh and calf muscles before beginning may be advisable as well.

Warm-Up

The athletes stand 20 feet apart facing each other in a ready position (knees bent, hands out ready to catch or throw a ball). General room lighting is acceptable; brighter room lighting makes this exercise less difficult. Shoulders and hips remain parallel to each other as much as possible throughout the whole exercise.

The athletes begin tossing the tennis ball back and forth to each other. The athletes should focus their eyes on the ball as it is traveling. The throws should be to all nine quadrants (top right, top center, top left, middle right, middle center, middle left, lower right, lower center, lower left), using both the left and right hands to throw and catch. They should catch the ball with the hand that is on the same side as the throw (unless it is intentionally a cross-catch, which can be incorporated later to add difficulty). The goal is to allow each participant to catch the ball, so care should be taken to start with slow, direct throws that are not bounces. If an athlete misses a catch, he or she retrieves the ball as quickly as possible and resumes throwing. As the athletes get comfortable with a level, they can increase the difficulty by increasing the speed. Follow the list below:

1. Slow non-bouncing throws
2. Slow bouncing throws (Bounces can be both high and low. Make sure to direct them to all nine quadrants of gaze.)
3. Speed up both non-bouncing and bouncing throws
4. Incorporate bouncing the ball off of walls
5. Start crossing over the midline by using the right hand to catch on the left side and the left hand to catch on the right. It is extremely important to keep the shoulders and hips parallel. One of the goals of this exercise is for the athletes to train their athletic movements while keeping a forward stance.
6. Have the athletes move closer together
7. Have the athletes catch the ball with just the thumb, index finger, and middle finger

*Please note:*

It is important to incorporate throws to all nine quadrants of gaze during this game of catch. Special emphasis should be put on the quadrants that are areas of weakness for the athlete. You can change the color of the ball to increase the level of difficulty. Start with green and move to red, blue, and then black.

Variations: As the athlete becomes proficient, begin to incorporate the following variations to increase the level of difficulty. Begin at the top of the list, master that variation, and move to the next level of difficulty. I have included 11 variations.

Ball Toss: Lunge

In this variation, one athlete works out by catching the ball while the other athlete acts as the trainer. The trainer remains in the ready position throughout and throws the ball to the athlete, who is working out.

The athlete who is going to catch the ball starts by lunging forward with his right foot as the ball is thrown to one of the quadrants on the athlete's right side. As he throws the ball back to the trainer, the athlete returns to the ready position. The athlete continues to lunge forward with the right foot as the ball is thrown to different areas in the nine quadrants. After five throws, the athlete lunges forward with the left foot for five throws. The athlete should continue alternating sides for five lunges until a sufficient workout of all quadrants is complete.

Throughout this sequence, the athlete should keep the shoulders and pelvis square and high. This actively recruits the transverse abdominis and multifidus muscles. The athlete starts off with shorter lunges, then continues to increase the difficulty for the hips and shoulders with longer lunges. To do this, the trainer uses shorter throws so that the ball gets further and further from the midline of the athlete's body, forcing him to stretch for each catch.

Additional variations to incorporate:

1. Front-lunge catch to same hand
2. Front-lunge catch to opposite or trailing hand
3. Side lunge to same hand
4. Side lunge to trailing hand
5. Back lunge to same hand
6. Back lunge to trailing hand
7. Front crossover lunge, throw is to the same side as the lunge

and the catch is with the opposite side hand. (The trainer throws to the athlete's left side while the athlete lunges with the right leg crossing over the midline to the left side and catches with the right hand extended in front of his body to the far left side.)

8. Front crossover lunge: the throw is to the same side as the lunge and the catch is with the same side hand. (The trainer throws to the athlete's left side while the athlete lunges with the right leg crossing over the midline to the left side and catches with the left hand extended.)

9. Back crossover

The lunge exercise is for the muscles, so throws should be made so that the athlete can catch the ball successfully. As the level of difficulty increases by using an increased range of motion in each lunge, the throws should slow down and bouncing should be eliminated so that the body can have fluid and complete movement. (Example: If Variation 8 is tried, the ball should be thrown directly to the athlete's hand.) Again, care should be taken to work on all nine quadrants of the athlete's body.

### Ball Toss: Friesen Off-Wall React Drill

In this variation, the athlete stands 15 feet from a wall, facing it, with shoulders and hips parallel in a ready position. The trainer in this exercise stands around 15 feet behind the athlete. The trainer then throws the ball at the wall in front of the athlete. The athlete responds by catching the ball as it bounces off the wall and back at him. Throws continue so that all quadrants are worked out. The speed of the ball can be increased to increase difficulty.

### Ball Toss: Cullen Closed-Eyes Off-Wall Drill

This variation has the athlete stand ready but with her eyes closed. The trainer throws the ball against the wall. The athlete opens her eyes the second she hears the ball hit the wall. The athlete then has to quickly find the ball and catch it. This should be repeated several times, as above.

### Ball Toss: Ward Quick Hands

In this variation the athlete and trainer stand about 10 feet apart, facing each other. The trainer throws the ball to the athlete's nondominant hand. The athlete then bounces the ball from the nondominant hand to catch it with the dominant hand and then bounces it back to the trainer. Speed is increased. Rotation can be reversed. Having the athlete incorporate a bounce off of the back of her hand can increase the difficulty. The athlete follows the ball with her eyes during this exercise. At some point, when the athlete gets a good feel for the distance to the trainer and the speed of the throws, she can close her eyes and try to perform this exercise by feel.

### Ball Toss: Ward Fakeout

This variation of the Ball Toss: Ward Quick Hands exercise has the trainer trying to fake out the athlete as to where the throw will be. The athlete focuses on the sternum of the trainer. The trainer then jabs the throw in many different directions before finally releasing the ball. Speed can be increased to increase difficulty.

### Ball Toss: Acuity Drill

Use a black permanent marker to place one-inch letters on the ball (six letters altogether, at the north/east/west/south positions and the top and bottom). Perform any of the above variations, but have the athlete concentrate on reading a letter before catching the ball. This helps the athlete improve his concentration level and will also improve dynamic visual acuity.

### Ball Toss: Concentrate on Core

In this variation, the athlete catches and returns the ball while sitting on a workout mat or balancing ball or while lying on the mat. The trainer needs to throw the ball at a slower speed and can target specific weaker areas in the athlete.

### Ball Toss: Strobe Glasses/Strobe Light

(Do not perform this variation if the athlete suffers from seizures.)

This variation works to develop mental concentration as well as improving eye-hand coordination. Perform any of the above variations in a room with a strobe light going or while the athlete wears strobe glasses. Turn the strobe on at a fast level and begin throwing the ball to the athlete. Slow down the speed of the strobe so that it becomes difficult. After two to three minutes, turn off the strobe and turn on the regular room lights while continuing the exercise. The athlete is likely to notice that the ball immediately appears to be larger and moving slower. This mimics being in the zone.

### Ball Toss: Perturbation

Degree of difficulty can be greatly increased by adding perturbation to any of the above exercises. This is accomplished by having a second trainer stand behind the athlete while he trains with any of the previous variations. The second trainer physically pulls or pushes on the athlete who is training, to throw him off. This distraction greatly increases concentration and physical prowess. The second trainer can also use a foam-rubber therapy roll to hit the athlete's body or quickly flash it in front of his eyes, to add more physical and visual noise in this variation.

### Ball Toss: Four-Corner Shuffle

This variation adds work on lower-body coordination to the ball exercises. Use chalk or tape on the floor to make a square measuring three feet by three feet. Then, add a horizontal line and a vertical line in the middle so that you've sectioned the big square into four smaller squares.

The athlete stands with his or her feet in the front two squares and begins to shuffle her feet so that the right leg moves to the back square, the left leg moves to the back square, the right leg moves to the front square, the left leg moves to the front square, and then the process repeats over and over while the trainer starts general throws to the athlete. The trainer can then add different variations of throws, as in the Ball Toss: Warm-Up. The athlete can also change the leg-shuffle pattern by standing in the front squares and hopping to the back squares and then hopping back to the front squares or by starting with the left leg in the front square and the right leg in the back square and hopping to switch the left leg to the back square and the right leg to the front square and then hop back to the original position and start again.

### Ball Toss: General Throws

This final variation on the exercise really increases the difficulty. This is similar to the Ball Toss: Warm-Up, but after the athlete is warmed up and flexibility has been achieved, she can push to reach higher reaction times and increase core temperature for competition. In this part of the exercise, each athlete tries to better the other with the throws.

Start with general throws and slowly increase the speed. Low bouncing balls to ankle height are great warm-ups at the beginning of the exercise. Increase difficulty by increasing speed and by throwing lower "skims" off the floor.

**Juggling Drill**

Group: EH

Objective: This exercise is used to:

- Increase concentration/focus
- Improve eye-hand coordination
- Improve peripheral awareness

Equipment: Three beanbags or small balls

Instructions: Learn to juggle three beanbags. There are many websites on the Internet that do a better job of teaching this skill than I can. This is a hard skill to learn but very beneficial in terms of achieving this exercise's objectives.

Variations: As the athlete becomes proficient in this exercise, begin to incorporate these variations to increase the level of difficulty. Begin at the top of the list, master that variation, and move to the next level of difficulty.

- Have the athlete move while juggling.
- Ask the athlete to jump up and down while juggling.
- Hold cards with numbers to the athlete's side while he juggles. Have the athlete use his side vision to determine what number is on the card.

**Soccer Ball/Hacky Sack Juggle**

Group: EH

Objective: To improve eye-hand-body coordination

Equipment: Soccer ball or hacky sack

Instructions: The athlete stands in place and begins kicking the soccer ball with the right leg in such a manner that the soccer ball rises about two feet and then drops to an area over the left foot. The athlete then kicks the soccer ball in the same manner with the left foot so that it returns to its original spot over the right foot. The athlete continues this pattern for the training session.

There are several sites on the Internet for the athlete to learn how to juggle with the feet. This is also a great way to increase core body temperature for competition.

**Four/Seven-Card Game**

Group: ME

Objective: To improve visual memory

Equipment: Up to seven playing cards, a table, a swivel chair, and a training partner

Instructions: The athlete sits in a chair that rotates and begins by facing away from the table. The trainer places four to seven cards in a line on the table face up. The athlete revolves to see the cards briefly and then revolves away. The athlete then tells the trainer what cards were showing.

If a swivel chair is not available, the trainer can hold his hands over the athlete's eyes and continue the exercise like a game of peek-a-boo. The trainer can also hold a book or papers a couple inches over the cards so that they are hidden from view, quickly remove it so the cards are visible, and then cover the cards back up so that the athlete only has a second to view the cards. The athlete then must recite the values and order of the cards that he or she just read.

The goal is to increase the number of cards that the athlete can accurately remember, including the order in which the cards appeared.

**Scrabble Pieces Memory Game**

Group: ME

Objective: To improve visual memory

Equipment: 30 to 50 Scrabble pieces, note cards, the floor or a table, and a training partner

This exercise requires a little setup. Put the Scrabble pieces in 10 different stations of four or five letters apiece, face up and oriented in the same direction. Place note cards over the letters at each station. Have the trainer show the athlete the letters at one of the stations for one second and then cover them again. The athlete recites the letters back to the trainer and moves on to the next station. Increase the number of pieces at each station to increase difficulty. The athlete can look directly at the letters or, as a variation, the athlete can fixate on a spot in the middle of the table and use his or her side vision to determine the letters.

**Visualization**

Group: ME

Objective: To mentally prepare for competition

Equipment: A quiet place

Instructions: The athlete sits or lies in a comfortable, quiet place with eyes closed and a cleared mind. The athlete uses the mind's eye to see herself performing an athletic endeavor. First the athlete pictures herself performing at the level where she's currently performing and then improving to a slightly higher level. The athlete should not fantasize or perform feats that she

cannot perform in real life; the athlete should not visualize negatives outcomes, either, but picture every type of realistic scenario
and the reactions to those different scenarios. The athlete visualizes possible sources of visual noise and her reactions to those
distractions. The athlete includes how she is feeling physically
during this time and how she can push herself further. The athlete sees what her opponents are doing and how they are reacting to her actions. The athlete visualizes success.

Visualize the action from two different perspectives:
- From the athlete's perspective, as though she is seeing
  everything around her during the scenarios
- From the perspective of a spectator who is watching the
  athlete perform

**Relaxation**

Group: ME

Objective: To improve the athlete's ability to control his or her
thoughts and to find a place of calm to use during competition

Equipment: A quiet place

Instructions: The athlete sits or lies down on his back and
stays perfectly still, with eyes closed. The athlete imagines that
he is by himself at the beach on a warm and beautiful day. The
athlete feels the heat from the sun as it shines down on him, feels
the warmth as it moves over him. The athlete hears the sound of
the waves as they rush in and then rush out. The athlete imagines
floating on a raft on those waves and enjoys the relaxing motion
of the waves. The athlete lets his body and muscles get really
loose and relaxed.

The athlete takes a deep breath in and holds it for a count
of five, then releases it, feeling the toxins in his body start to
leave. The athlete takes another breath and does the same, then

repeats several times, feeling his heartbeat as it relaxes and his heart rate decrease. The athlete allows himself to think only about his breathing and his heart rate as he listens to and feels the motion of the ocean waves in the background. The athlete continues deep, slow breathing while visualizing the toxins in his body leaving.

The athlete starts to feel a wave of relaxation go over his body. The athlete is heading to a place of calm. The athlete feels the wave of relaxation as it hits his right big toe. He can feel how the wave comes and goes over his toe. He can feel a tingling and warmth in his toe. Now, the wave of relaxation slowly moves up to the arch of his foot. He can feel it as it continues to move and it slowly crawls up the calf of his leg. He can actually feel the calf muscle relax. Now it's over his thigh and he can feel it as that muscle relaxes. He can feel the tingle as it moves to the back part of his leg and slowly moves up to his lower back. He can feel the tingle as every muscle relaxes. Now the wave of relaxation is at his right shoulder. He can feel the shoulders as they loosen and relax and feel his neck as it slowly starts to release that tension. The athlete lets it relax and loosen. Now the back of his neck feels the tingle of relief. He allows this tingle to continue for a while. Many of us hold a majority of our stress in our neck muscles, so this area needs more time to relax. Now, the athlete feels the tingle move down the muscles of his right arm, from his biceps and triceps down to his forearm and then into each individual finger. Then he feels the tingle as it crawls back up and across his neck to his left shoulder and then down through his left arm. Now he feels it crawl up his arm and back out to his chest. He feels it move slowly over his body as it goes to the upper left leg. He feels it move around to the back of his leg, down to his calf, down to his ankle, down to his toe. Now it leaves, and he is totally relaxed and in a place of calm.

This state of relaxation is very important for an athlete's mind and his body. It gives his mind a break from its day-to-day overload; it is a chance to release, cleanse, and reboot. The mind also gets to reconnect with the body as it becomes in tune with the workings of the muscles, lungs, and heart. The body enjoys this state because the heart rate is decreased and the heart doesn't have to work as hard. Blood pressure is lowered. The tension held in the muscles is relieved, and blood flow to the muscles is improved. Stress has been removed.

The following is the DVZ Improver for the Chart Read Exercise on page 252. A full-sized copy is available for download on www.seetoplay.com.

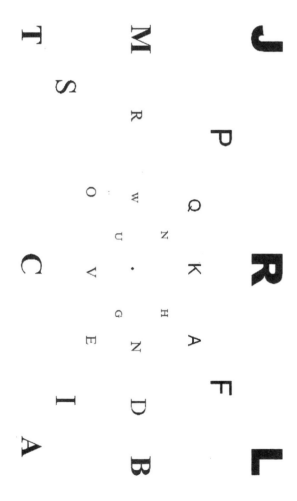

# CHAPTER 13
## SEE TO PLAY RANKING METHOD

In this book, I've described the measurable traits that I used to develop a method of ranking athletes by their vision. I also use this method to evaluate prospective athletes and predict where they may fall in comparison to other athletes. In this chapter, I will explain the components of this method. I will also go over how I score the findings that I use to derive the final ranking.

The results of the visual-acuity and side-vision measurements comprise two-thirds of the total points of the athlete's score. Eye alignment, as measured using two different methods, and scores for eye focusing and eye-hand coordination make up the rest of an athlete's vision score. These measurements and the way I weight the scores are:

A. **Visual Acuity**: Athletes are ranked in order of who has the best acuity with both eyes open, from first to worst. If there is a tie between athletes, I use the monocular findings (right-eye acuity and left-eye acuity) as a tie-breaker. The rankings are then multiplied by four to get the athletes' scores. Acuity is weighted the most in the scoring method, so you will notice a multiplication factor.

B. **Detailed Vision Range**: Athletes are ranked by the size of their ranges, with larger ranges ranked higher. A multiplier (x2) is used to get the score for this measurement as well.

C. **Extreme Side Vision**: Athletes are ranked by the size of their zones, with larger zones ranked higher. A multiplier (x2) is also used to get the score for this measurement.

D. **Eye Alignment of Aiming**: Measured using the Farnsworth method described in Chapter 4.

E. **Eye Alignment on Object**: Measured using the Brock string method.

F. **Eye Focusing:** Scores are taken from the Speed-Focus Read exercise found in Chapter 5.

G. **Eye-Hand Coordination**: Scores are from an eye-hand reaction board. Reminder: Athletes should have an equal chance to practice this test to assure the validity of the findings.

**Example**

As an example, I'll use a team consisting of five athletes. Each player is ranked according to the seven categories listed above. The rankings are established by comparing their results, and they are given one point per rank. (First place gets one point, second place gets two points, third place gets three points, etc.) Players who tie are given the points for the place that they tied (if tied for second, both get two points). Ties are indicated by a *(t)* beside the number of points, so that tied for third place appears in the chart below as 3 (t).

The player with the lowest overall total points is ranked first, and then the other players are ranked in order from next lowest number of points to highest.

The chart that follows shows the five teammates who were tested, how the players ranked in each of the seven categories, the points that they scored from that ranking, and then their total scores.

| | A | Ax4 | B | Bx2 | C | Cx2 | D | E | F | G | Total Points |
|---|---|---|---|---|---|---|---|---|---|---|---|
| Player 1 Rank | 4 | | 5 | | 4 | | 4 | 1 (t) | 3 | 4 | |
| Points | | 16 | | 10 | | 8 | 4 | 1 | 3 | 4 | 46 |
| Player 2 Rank | 3 | | 2 | | 3 | | 1 (t) | 1 (t) | 2 | 1 | |
| Points | | 12 | | 4 | | 6 | 1 | 1 | 2 | 1 | 27 |
| Player 3 Rank | 5 | | 4 | | 2 | | 3 | 2 (t) | 5 | 5 | |
| Points | | 20 | | 8 | | 4 | 3 | 2 | 5 | 5 | 47 |
| Player 4 Rank | 2 | | 3 | | 5 | | 2 | 2 (t) | 1 | 3 | |
| Points | | 8 | | 6 | | 10 | 2 | 2 | 1 | 3 | 32 |
| Player 5 Rank | 1 | | 1 | | 1 | | 1 (t) | 1(t) | 4 | 2 | |
| Points | | 4 | | 2 | | 2 | 1 | 1 | 4 | 2 | 16 |

Player 5 has the lowest point total, so he or she is ranked as having the best visual system on the team. Player 2's ranking is second on the team. Player 4 is ranked third. Player 1 is ranked fourth, and Player 3 is ranked fifth.

The point totals do not reflect any information about how good or bad the visual system is for an individual athlete. This method was devised for comparison purposes only. I've had some trainers and coaches look at the total points and say, "Geez, that guy's numbers are so high, his eyes must be terrible." You cannot tell from the point system if the visual acuity of the players in the group ranged only from 20/10 to 20/20 or if it was a group of athletes with 20/20 to 20/200 vision. The score is just a tool for the tester to use to rank the players in relationship with each other.

As I mentioned earlier in this book, depth perception and dynamic visual acuity could be added as separate categories to aid in ranking athletes. With that said, if I had only two tests to use to predict which athletes may become elite, I would use visual acuity and the detailed vision zone.

We are all familiar with how athletes are judged physically. I believe that when athletes test high physically but can't seem to translate those high scores to great performances in the world of competition that it is the visual system that lets them down. There are times when athletes don't perform well on their physical tests but still find a way to compete at a high level, and in those cases again I believe that their visual systems play an important role in pushing them to the top.

This ranking method gives a definitive way to assess whether or not athletes have the complete visual system that will give them the chance to see to play.

# EPILOGUE

This book has been a labor of love. I'm just a small-town boy who had a dream to be an elite athlete. As I grew up, my dreams were affected by the fact that my eyes were not able to perform at their optimum level. This didn't squash my dreams; it changed them. It allowed me to appreciate what it takes to become an elite athlete. It made me question how I could help others achieve this goal.

I am a sports-vision specialist. Through my years of working with the best of the best, I have developed a program that has helped make the best better. I wrote this book to share it with small-town boys and girls everywhere and with the parents, coaches, trainers, and helpers of those potential elite athletes. You are now equipped with my program, my 16 See to Play tips, and exercises that will help you maximize your athletic potential.

Whether you're preparing for a grade school soccer match, a high school varsity game, or the biggest moment in your career as a professional athlete or trainer, I hope you have used my tools to your advantage. May you play well and **see to play!**

# ACKNOWLEDGMENTS

I feel very privileged for the affiliations that I've had with sports teams in the Raleigh, NC, area, their athletes, and the doctors and health care providers who have contributed to each team's sports-medicine program. I want to acknowledge them because they have been an integral part of my development as a health care provider and, ultimately, their input has helped me develop how I work with athletes. I hope all of you in the sports community have a chance to work with great people in all areas of specialties and I urge you, for the sake of the athletes, to become networked in the work you may be doing to help them.

I'd particularly like to thank the following organizations and individuals:

- Alison Hodges, editor. How does an eye doctor write a book about elite athletes? It takes the expertise of an elite editor!
- Stephen Bolick, OD, chairman and CEO of Eye Care Associates
- Jason Price, OD, my right hand in our sports-vision program and one of the brightest optometrists in practice
- Robert Brodney, president of Eye Care Associates
- Brian Hoyle, director of marketing for ECA
- Adam Peters, for his advice and help in this process
- The Carolina Hurricanes organization, including:

–Peter Friesen: I can't say enough to thank him for his input into my approach to working with athletes

–Pete's assistant trainers Stu Lemke, Chris Stewart, Jason Bailey, and Doug Bennett

–Peter Karmanos Jr., owner; Jim Rutherford, general manager; and Jason Karmanos, assistant general manager; head coaches Paul Maurice and Peter Laviolette and assistant coaches Tom Barrasso, Ron Francis, Tom Rowe, Rod Brind'Amour, Glen Wesley, Jeff Daniels, Kevin McCarthy, and Randy Ladouceur

–Team physicians Hadley Callaway, MD, Marty Isbell, MD, and Jeremy Stinson, PA, of the Raleigh Orthopaedic Clinic; Douglas Martini, MD, of Cary Orthopaedics; and Jay Stevens, MD, Josh Bloom, MD, Sandeep Gavankar, DO, Jim Blount, MD, Brett Foreman, MD, Aaron West, ATC, and Janna Fonseca, ATC, from Carolina Family Practice and Sports Medicine

- The Durham Bulls baseball team (yes, like in the movie *Bull Durham*)

–Orthopedist Richard Bruch, MD

- The Tampa Bay Rays organization, including:

–Trainers Joe Benge, Rodger Fleming, Mark Vinson, Tom Tisdale, and Paul Harker

–Coaches Charlie Montoyo, Xavier Hernandez, and Bill Evers

- The Atlanta Braves organization, particularly trainers Dave Tomchek and Jay Williams
- The Carolina Mudcats owner Steve Bryant and general manger Joe Kramer
- The Pittsburgh Pirates organization and trainer Sandy Krum

- The Colorado Rockies organization and trainer Travis Anderson
- The Florida Marlins organization
- The Cincinnati Reds organization, including:
  –Trainers Charles Leddon and Jimmy Mattocks
  –Orthopedist Mark Galland, MD
- The Carolina Cobras of the Arena Football League and trainer Herman Bunch
- The Raleigh RailHawks and head trainer Lizy Coleman
- The Raleigh Wings professional women's soccer team
- The US national baseball team and USA Baseball
- The North Carolina State University Wolfpack and head trainer Charlie Rozanski
- Duke University, especially Jeffrey R. Bytomski, DO, and trainer Andrew Norden
- The University of North Carolina at Chapel Hill and Director of Sports Nutrition Jennifer Ketterly, MS, RD, CSSD
- Wakefield High School coach Brent Dorenkamp; orthopedist Shepherd Rosenblum, MD; and physical therapist Chris Walters, PT
- The Capital Area Soccer League
- The people from Hillcrest Media helped me with the process of turning this manuscript into a book. Everyone I worked with was incredible.

I'm very fortunate to be a partner at one of the leading eye-care providers in the nation, Eye Care Associates, which is currently one of the top 20 largest eye-care providers in the United States. We have a great group of doctors who have really helped me develop our sports-vision program, starting with Caroline

Silver, OD, and Benjamin Lee, OD. Monica Reeves, OD, has been instrumental in helping me develop my philosophy on core and physical workouts. Jeff Strand, OD, has helped me with our work with the Carolina Mudcats. I can't begin to thank and name all of the countless associates of ECA who have helped me through the years. I do want to thank my sports-vision therapists Ashley Moore, Allie Bolick, Carrie Williams, and Anna Morgan.

I'd also like to thank the ophthalmologists who have helped me with athletes: Karl Stonecipher, MD; Paul Riske, MD; Raynor Casey, MD; and Charles Efrig, MD.

I'd like to thank my parents, who have always been my biggest source of support, especially during the time when I made the decision to leave the football field and move in the direction of becoming an eye doctor.

And a very special thanks to my wife and daughters for putting up with me during this project. This journey took me four years, and I wasn't sure I really had it in me. My family has had to hear me blather on about this topic ("Oh, I just finished a chapter!" "Oh, I think this is a great idea!" and on and on…), and I can't thank them enough for their love and support.

I hope all of you will join me to help athletes see to play. I know personally how frustrating it is to be weeded out of a sport you love because of your eyes. I also know how exhilarating it can be to fix a deficiency in an athlete's visual system and then watch as an elite athlete develops and goes on to win at the highest of levels.

I plan to provide updates to the information you've found in this book on my web page. Feel free to check out the latest happenings on www.seetoplay.com, and visit www.ecanc.com for information on High Performance Vision.

# SEE TO PLAY TIPS

# GLOSSARY

| | |
|---|---|
| **Aberration** | A distortion of an image that travels through the optical system and causes the image to be blurred compared to the original object. See Chapter 2, "Superhuman Acuity." |
| **Accommodation** | The action of the internal lens system of the eye to focus on a near object in order to see it clearly. The ability to accommodate lessens naturally after the age of 40. See Chapter 5, "Fast Focus Finishes First." |
| **Accommodation Insufficiency** | A condition in which the muscles in charge of making the eye's internal lens system are sluggish or weak, causing decreased ability to focus clearly on objects that are near. See Chapter 5, "Fast Focus Finishes First." |
| **Amblyopia** | A condition in which vision in an eye does not develop better than 20/40 because of an eye turn, an uncorrected prescription, or genetics, and as a result the brain doesn't use the eye for visual acuity. Patch therapy between two to six years of age can help train the amblyopic eye to see with better acuity. See Chapter 2, "Superhuman Acuity." |
| **Amplitude of Accommodation** | The point at which a person's strength of focusing is at its maximum. See Chapter 5, "Fast Focus Finishes First." |

| | |
|---|---|
| **Aqueous** | The fluid between the cornea and iris that keeps the cornea dome-shaped. A puncture of the cornea can cause this fluid to leak out. See Chapter 10, "Eye Injuries." |
| **Astigmatism** | A condition in which the front part of the eye–the cornea–has the shape of a football or cone instead of being round like a basketball. See Chapter 2, "Superhuman Acuity." |
| **Best Corrected Acuity** | Measured acuity that is the best possible. The athlete may have to wear their fullest prescription in order to achieve this state. See Chapter 2, "Superhuman Acuity." |
| **Brock String** | A string with three beads that is used to test horizontal eye alignment and as a tool to train eye-muscle strength. See Chapter 12, "See to Play Vision Exercises." |
| **Cones** | Photoreceptors in the macula responsible for 20/20 vision. See Chapter 3, "See Wide for Champion Side Vision." |
| **Convergence** | The motion of moving the eyes so that they both rotate in toward the nose, similar to the act of crossing one's eyes. See Chapter 4, "Move Your Eyes!" |
| **Convergence Insufficiency (CI)** | The inability to bring your eyes completely in toward each other or turn your eyes in enough that they are both pointing at a near object. See Chapter 4, "Move Your Eyes!" |

**Cornea**

Clear, dome-shaped tissue on the very front of the eye and iris that light first travels through when entering the eye. See Chapter 2, "Superhuman Acuity."

**Cross-Dominancy**

A right-handed athlete whose left eye is the dominant eye or a left-handed athlete whose right eye is the dominant eye exhibits cross-dominancy. See Chapter 4, "Move Your Eyes!"

**Depth Perception**

The ability of two eyes to work together as a team to determine the distance of an object from the body. See Chapter 2, "Superhuman Acuity."

**Diffuse Axonal Injury**

An injury to the brain that causes disruption to neurotransmission. See Chapter 10, "Eye Injuries."

**Dominancy**

The eye the brain prefers to use the more than the other is the dominant eye. See Chapter 4, "Move Your Eyes!"

**Dorsal Visual Stream**

The vision pathway involved with spatial awareness, detecting and analyzing movements, and learning of eye-hand-body coordination. See Chapter 3, "See Wide for Champion Side Vision."

**Dynamic Visual Acuity**

Visual acuity measured on a rotating chart that gives the tester some idea of how well athletes can distinguish moving objects. See Chapter 2, "Superhuman Acuity."

**Elite Athletes** — The group of athletes who have reached the "best of the best" level. Athletes who have made it to a professional sports team such as the NFL, NBA, NHL, MLB, professional soccer, or the PGA or LPGA. People who represent their nation in an Olympic sport. See Chapter 1, "Only the Best Eyes Make It."

**Eye-Hand-Body Coordination** — The act of the athlete's eye seeing something, the brain deciding the proper response, and then responding to that stimulus with motion of a hand or body part. See Chapter 6, "Eye-Hand-Body Coordination."

**Farsightedness** — Also known as hyperopia. The ability to see objects more clearly at a distance than up close without correction due to a shorter length of the eye or a flatter cornea. See Chapter 2, "Superhuman Acuity."

**Fixed-Space Eye Exercises** — Vision exercises that use equipment and machines that aren't portable. Usually found in an eye doctor's office. See Chapter 6, "Eye-Hand-Body Coordination."

**Fovea** — The area in the center of the retina where images are focused and formed. This area is responsible for 20/20 vision. Also known as the macula. See Chapter 3, "See Wide for Champion Side Vision."

**Free-Space Eye Exercises** — Vision exercises that are performed in an open space and that are portable. See Chapter 6, "Eye-Hand-Body Coordination."

| | |
|---|---|
| **Fusion** | The ability to see a complete object image staying together as the eyes converge inward rather than seeing it splitting into two. Losing fusion, or seeing a double image, is the result of convergence insufficiency. See Chapter 4, "Move Your Eyes!" |
| **High-Performance Vision Exercises** | Vision therapy that incorporates sport-specific training. See Chapter 1, "Only the Best Eyes Make It." |
| **Hyperopia** | See Farsightedness. |
| **Involuntary Nervous System** | The system that controls your breathing, heart, and other body functions that do not require conscious control. See Chapter 6, "Eye-Hand-Body Coordination." |
| **Iris** | The colored part of eye, which has the pupil in the center. See Chapter 5, "Fast Focus Finishes First." |
| **Keratoconus** | An astigmatism that keeps growing; the football shape of the cornea just keeps moving further and further out. See Chapter 2, "Superhuman Acuity." |
| **Macula** | The area in the center of the retina where images are focused. This area is responsible for 20/20 vision and contains cones. Also called the fovea. See Chapter 2, "Superhuman Acuity," and Chapter 3, "See Wide for Champion Side Vision." |
| **Monocular** | The use of only one eye to see. See Chapter 2, "Superhuman Acuity." |
| **Myopia** | See Nearsightedness. |

**Nearsightedness**    Also known as myopia. Vision is clearer on objects up close and blurry on objects at a distance. Usually due to a longer eyeball length or steeper curve in the cornea. See Chapter 2, "Superhuman Acuity."

**Orbital Blowout Fracture**    A hole in the floor of the orbit caused by blunt force to the eye. See Chapter 10, "Eye Injuries."

**Ophthalmology**    A medical specialization in surgery and the treatment of eye diseases. See the introduction.

**Optometry**    Eye-care professionals who specialize in refractions and the fitting of contacts and glasses and in vision therapy. See the introduction.

**Perturbation**    Physical contact designed to cause interference during an activity, such as an exercise. See Chapter 12, "See to Play Vision Exercises."

**Proprioception**    The system in charge of letting our bodies know about orientation in space, movement, and balance. Includes vision, the inner ear, and sensors on muscles and joints in our body. See Chapter 6, "Eye-Hand-Body Coordination."

**Pupil**    The black hole in the iris allowing light to travel back to the photoreceptors in the retina. See Chapter 2, "Superhuman Acuity."

**Receptors**    Rods and cones. They receive an image and transmit it to the brain. See Chapter 3, "See Wide for Champion Side Vision."

**Refraction**

The process of determining a prescription in the eye-exam room. See Chapter 2, "Superhuman Acuity."

**Retina**

The layer of tissue that holds photoreceptors responsible for seeing an image and transporting it to the nervous system and ultimately the brain. See Chapter 2, "Superhuman Acuity."

**Rods**

Photoreceptors in the retina responsible for night vision and picking up motion. See Chapter 3, "See Wide for Champion Side Vision."

**Same-Side Dominancy**

Right-hand dominant and right-eye dominant athletes and left-hand dominant and left-eye dominant athletes exhibit same-side cominancy. See Chapter 4, "Move Your Eyes!"

**Toric**

Contact lenses that are made to treat astigmatism. See Chapter 2, "Superhuman Acuity."

**Valsalva Maneuver**

A forceful breath held in by pushing up against the glottis during exertion that causes intrathoracic or intra-abdominal pressure to increase, causing intraocular venous pressure, which in turn can cause a rupture in the superficial retinal capillaries. See Chapter 10, "Eye Injuries."

**Ventral Visual Stream**

Visual pathway responsible for object recognition, form recognition, assigning importance to objects, and governing working memory, attention, and conscious pathways. See Chapter 3, "See Wide for Champion Side Vision."

**Vision Therapy**  Eye exercises to help eye muscles work better or to help the eyes work better as a team. See Chapter 4, "Move Your Eyes!"

**Visual Acuity**  Standard measurement of how well someone sees in detail. See Chapter 2, "Superhuman Acuity."

**Voluntary Nervous System**  The parts of your brain that are in charge of your actions and motions. See Chapter 6, "Eye-Hand-Body Coordination."

**Yoked Prism**  Lenses that bend light in such a way that the object being viewed appears to shift and move in relation to spatial location. See Chapter 7, "Visual Noise."

# REFERENCES

## Chapter 1: Only the Best Eyes Make It

Associated Press. "Got Game in 7th Grade? NCAA Says You're a Prospect." *ESPN.com.* Last updated January 16, 2009. http://sports.espn.go.com/ncb/news/story?id=3837197 (accessed October 7, 2010).

Black, Amy. "Realizing the Potential of Progressive Lenses." *Review of Optometry.* 15 Dec. 2003.

"Busy week a sign of the times for top prospect Hamilton." *The News and Observer,* 26 May 1999, sec. C, p. 5.

Coffey, Bradley, and Alan W. Reichow, "Optometric Evaluation of the Elite Athlete." *Problems in Optometry* 2.1 (1990): 32–59.

Koenig, Bill. "In Every Sense, Williams Saw More Than Most." *USA Today Baseball Weekly*, 1 May 1996, May 8–14 Edition ed.: 35.

Koenig, Bill. "Practicing Perception: Eyes Can Be Trained to Be More Effective." *USA TODAY Baseball Weekly*, May 1, 1996.

Leadbetter, David. "Michelle Is Right to Turn Professional." http://www.telegraph.co.uk/sport/golf/womensgolf/2366336/Michelle-is-right-to-turn-professional.html (accessed March 25, 2011).

Mair, Lewane. "Woosnam Keen to Follow Faldo's Current Trend." http://www.telegraph.co.uk/sport/golf/2372493/Woosnam-keen-to-follow-Faldos-current-trend.html (accessed

March 25, 2011).

Meir, Rudi. "Conditioning the Visual System: A Practical Perspective on Visual Conditioning in Rugby Football." *Strength and Conditioning Journal* 27.4 (2005): 86–92.

National Football League. "Workouts & Drills." http://www. nfl.com/combine/workouts (accessed October 7, 2010).

Newlin, Chris. "Estimated Probability of Competing in Athletics Beyond the High School Interscholastic Level." http://www.ncaa.org/wps/portal/ncaahome?WCM_GLOBAL_ CONTEXT=/ncaa/ncaa/academics and athletes/education and research/probability of competing/methodology - prob of competing (accessed October 7, 2010).

Seymour, Gene. "The Eyes Have It for Bears Quarterback." *Herald-News* [Joliet, Illinois] 4 Nov. 1990.

Vitale, Susan, Robert D. Sperduta, and Frederick L. Ferris. "Increased Prevalence of Myopia in the United States Between 1971–1972 and 1999–2004." *Archives of Ophthalmology* 127.12 (2009): 1632–1639.

**Chapter 2: Superhuman Acuity**

Bergman, Laurie. "Keeping McGwire's Eyes on Ball Takes Teamwork." *AOA News* 21 (September 1998): 1+.

Boden, Lauren, Kenneth Rosengren, Daniel Martin, and Scott Boden. "A Comparison of Static Near Stereo Acuity in Youth Baseball/Softball Players and Non-Ball Players." *Journal of the American Optometric Association* 80.3 (2009): 121–25.

Colliano, Daria Del. "Brian McCann Hopes Glasses Will Be Solution To Eye Problems." *Bleacher Report: Entertaining Sports News, Photos and Slideshows*. May 7, 2009. http://bleacherreport.com/articles/169382-in-the-eye-of-the-beholder (accessed October 22, 2010).

Ferguson, Doug. "The Eyes of a Tiger Are Finally Adjusted." *USATODAY.com: News, Travel, Weather, Entertainment, Sports, Technology, U.S. & World.* May 15 2007. http://www.usatoday.com/sports/golf/2007-05-15-3245505588_x.htm (accessed October 22, 2010).

Laby, Daniel M., Arthur Rosenbaum, et al. "The Visual Function of Professional Baseball Players." *American Journal of Ophthalmology* 122 (October 1996). 476-485.

Kirschen, David, Daniel, M. Laby, Matthew P. Kirschen, Raymond Applegate, and Larry N. Thibos. "Optical aberrations in professional baseball players." *Journal of Cataract and Refract Surgery* 36 (2010). 396-401.

Knudson, Duane, and Diane Kluka. "Vision and Sport Performance." http://www.sportsci.org/news/ferret/visionreview/visionreview.html (accessed October 22, 2010).

Kopp, J. David. "Eye on the Ball: An Interview with Dr. C. Stephen Johnson and Mark McGwire." *Journal of the American Optometric Association* 70.2 (1999): 79-84.

Neimark, Mark. "The Fight or Flight Response." http://www.thebodysoulconnection.com/EducationCenter/fight.html (accessed October 22, 2010).

"Statistics." *Coast-to-Coast Vision*™. Central New York Business Journal. (2005). http://coasttocoastvision.com/statistics.aspx (accessed October

22, 2010).

Thau, Andrea. "The Importance of Infant Eye Exams." *Review of Optometry* 15 (October 2009): 51+.

"Tiger Woods: TLC LASIK Success Story." http://www.tlcvision.com/why_famouspeople_tiger.fxml (accessed October 22, 2010).

Waldstein, David. "Hitters With Blue Eyes Are Wary About Glare." *The New York Times.* June 25, 2011. D2. http://www.nytimes.com/2011/06/25/sports/baseball/in-baseball-blue-eyed-hitters-are-wary-of-glare.html (accessed June 30, 2011).

Watt, Wendy Strouse. "How Visual Acuity Is Measured." *MD Support.* (October 2003). http://www.mdsupport.org/library/acuity.html (accessed October 22, 2010).

**Chapter 3: See Wide for Champion Side Vision**

Baumgard, Josh. "LeBron James vs. Larry Bird: Is King James More Complete Than Larry Legend?" *Bleacher Report: Entertaining Sports News, Photos and Slideshows.* February 8, 2011. http://bleacherreport.com/articles/601028-lebron-james-vs-larry-bird-is-lebron-more-versatile-than-larry-legend?source=rss_teams_Miami_Heat (accessed March 9, 2011).

Britt, Robert Roy. "Baseball Science: Better Hitters See Ball as Bigger." *LiveScience: Science, Technology, Health & Environmental News.* December 15, 2005. http://www.livescience.com/health/051215_ball_size.html (accessed October 22, 2010).

Dye, Lee. "Athletes in the Zone May See the World

Differently." *ABCNews.com - Breaking News, Politics, Online News, World News, Feature Stories, Celebrity Interviews and More.* August 5, 2008.
http://abcnews.go.com/Technology/AheadoftheCurve/story?id=5510786&page=1 (accessed October 22, 2010).

George, Thomas. "Jeff Fisher's Picture of Walter Payton? As Perfect Teammate." *NFL - Sporting News.* October 29, 2009.
http://nfl.fanhouse.com/2009/10/29/jeff-fishers-picture-of-walter-payton-as-perfect-teammate/ (accessed March 9, 2011)

McClain, Dylan L. "Harnessing the Brain's Right Hemisphere to Capture Many Kings." *The New York Times.* January 25, 2011.
http://www.nytimes.com/2011/01/25/science/25chess.html (accessed March 9, 2011).

Park, Alice. "Staying Sharp: Getting and Staying in the Zone." *Time.com: Breaking News, Analysis, Politics, Blogs, News Photos, Video, Tech Reviews.* January 8, 2006.
http://www.time.com/time/magazine/article/0,9171,1147173,00.html (accessed October 22, 2010).

Rappaport, Doug. "The Science of Peripheral Vision." *Sports Vision Magazine* 1.1 (2007): 28-31.

Schwartz, Larry. "ESPN.com: 'Great' and 'Gretzky' Belong Together." *ESPN: The Worldwide Leader In Sports.*
http://espn.go.com/sportscentury/features/00014218.html (accessed March 9, 2011).

Staff, ESPN.com. "Peyton Manning Bests Tom Brady in ESPN.com's Quarterback Voting." *ESPN: The Worldwide Leader In Sports.* November 19, 2010.
http://sports.espn.go.com/nfl/news/story?id=5819047 (accessed March 9, 2011).

Wertheim, Jon. "How Athletes Find the Zone." *SI.com: Breaking News, Real-time Scores and Daily Analysis from Sports Illustrated.* May 21, 2008. http://sportsillustrated. cnn.com/2008/writers/jon_wertheim/05/21/lardon/ (accessed October 22, 2010).

Young, Janet A., and Michelle D. Pain. "The Zone: An Empirical Study." *Athletic Insight - The Online Journal of Sport Psychology.* (1999). http://www.athleticinsight.com/Vol1Iss3/ Empirical_Zone.htm (accessed October 22, 2010).

**Chapter 4: Move Your Eyes!**

Classe, John, Kent Daum, Leo Semes, John Wisniewski, Robert Rustein, Larry Alexander, James Beisel, Kelly Mann, Rod Nowakowski, Mark Smith, and Albert Bartolucci. "Association Between Eye and Hand Dominance and Hitting, Fielding and Pitching Skill Among Players of the Southern Baseball League." *Sports Vision* 13.2 (1997): 32+.

Griffiths, Geraint. "Eye Dominance in Sports: A Comparative Study." *Optometry Today* 15 Aug. 2003: 34-40.

Laby, Daniel M., David G. Kirshchen, Arthur L. Rosenbaum, and Michael F. Mellman. "The Effect of Ocular Dominance on the Performance of Professional Baseball Players." *Ophthalmology* 105.5 (1998): 864-66.

Jones, III, Lewis, John Classe, Mark Hester, and Kevin Harris. "Association between Eye Dominance and Training for Rifle Marksmanship: A Pilot Study." *Journal of the American Optometric Association* 67.2 (1996): 73-76.

Meir, Rudi. "Conditioning the Visual System: A Practical Perspective on Visual Conditioning in Rugby Football." *National Strength and Conditioning Association* 27.4 (2005):

86-92.

Shipnuck, Alan. "2006 Masters Preview: Peaking Late -
03.29.06 - SI Vault." *SI.com: Breaking News, Real-time Scores
and Daily Analysis from Sports Illustrated.* March 29, 2006.
http://sportsillustrated.cnn.com/vault/article/web/
COM1047723/index.htm (accessed March 27, 2011).

Zuphan, Michael, and Al Wile. "Eyes on the Prize." *Training
and Conditioning* (March 2011): 11-15

**Chapter 6: Eye-Hand-Body Coordination**

A & E Television Networks. "John McEnroe Biography."
*Biography.com.* http://www.biography.com/articles/John-
McEnroe-9391860 (accessed October 22, 2010).

Adair, Robert K. *The Physics of Hitting a Baseball.* New York:
Harper-Collins Publishers, Inc.: 1990

"Ask Anything: 10 Questions with Soccer Star Mia Hamm"
*WRAL.com - Raleigh News, Weather, Triangle Traffic and
NC Lottery.* April 14, 2009. http://www.wral.com/news/local/
story/4947724/ (accessed March 9, 2011).

Associated Press. "Steffen Snatches Gold in 50m Free, Torres
Takes Silver - Olympics." *ESPN.com: The Worldwide Leader
In Sports.* August 17, 2008. http://sports.espn.go.com/oly/sum-
mer08/swimming/news/story?id=3539007 (accessed on October
22, 2010).

Forde, Pat. "Ranking Phelps' Eight Great Wins in Beijing -
Olympics." *ESPN.com: The Worldwide Leader In Sports.*
August 17 2008. http://sports.espn.go.com/oly/summer08/
columns/story?columnist=forde_pat&id=3539386 (accessed
October 22, 2010).

Fox, Larry. "Fantasy Time For Joe Montana." *Boy's Life Magazine.* November 1982: 28-31.

Fraser, Angus. "Don Bradman the World Beater." http://www.independent.co.uk/sport/cricket/don-bradman-the-world-beater-909527.html (accessed August 24, 2011).

Higdon, Hal. "Chang and Agassi: Courting Fame." *Boy's Life Magazine.* April 1989: 36-38.

Hirsch, James S. *Willie Mays: The Life, the Legend.* New York: Scribner, 2010.

Jordan, David. *Pete Rose: A Biography.* Westport: Greenwood, 2004.

Kilpatrick, J. E. "National AAU Swimming Electronic Timing and Judging Committee." 1975. TS. Minneapolis, Minnesota.

Kriegel, Mark. *Namath: A Biography.* New York: Penguin Group, 2005.

Montés-Micó, R., I. Bueno, J. Candel, and A. M. Pons. "Eye-Hand and Eye-Foot Visual Reaction Times of Young Soccer Players." *Optometry* 71.12 (2000): 775-80.

Roessing, Walter, and Douglass K. Daniel. Wayne's World. *Boy's Life Magazine.* March 1993. 13-14.

Sirimarco, Elizabeth. *Tiger Woods.* Mankato: Capstone, 2001.

UCSF Medical Center. "Medical Tests: Nerve Conduction Velocity." April 30, 2007. http://www.ucsfhealth.org/adult/adam/data/003927.html (accessed October 22, 2010).

Vascellaro, Charlie. *Hank Aaron: A Biography*. Westport: Greenwood, 2005.

Weyler, John. "Wade Boggs Surprises Opponents Only When He Doesn't Hit." *The Los Angeles Times*. May 14, 1986. http://articles.latimes.com/1986-05-14/sports/sp-5522_1_wade-boggs (accessed October 22, 2010)

**Chapter 7: Visual Noise**

Albergotti, Reed. "The NFL's Most Exciting Receiver - WSJ. com." *Business News & Financial News - The Wall Street Journal - WSJ.com*. January 16, 2009. http://online.wsj.com/article/SB123207803343289089.html (accessed October 22, 2010).

Dehesdin, Cecile. "Why Don't Figure Skaters Get Dizzy?" *Slate Magazine.* February 23, 2010. http://www.slate.com/id/2245775/ (accessed March 9, 2011).

Houser, Ben. "Arizona Cardinals' Larry Fitzgerald Makes Catching Look so Easy — Even with His Eyes Closed - ESPN." *ESPN: The Worldwide Leader In Sports*. August 18, 2009. http://sports.espn.go.com/espn/e60/news/story?id=4407415 (accessed October 22, 2010).

**Chapter 8: Using and Expanding Your Mind's Eye**

Balisunset. "Sport Psychology, Motivation and Performance." *HubPages*. http://balisunset.hubpages.com/hub/Sport-Psychology--Motivation-and-Performance (accessed October 22, 2010).

Bell, Buddy and Neal Vahle. Smart Baseball: *How Professionals Play the Mental Game.* New York: St. Martin's

Press, 2005, 49.

Christianson, Kiel. "Can Positive Imagery REALLY Help Your Golf Game?" *Plan and Book Your Golf Vacation with TravelGolf.com.* June 2, 2003. http://www.travelgolf.com/departments/clubhouse/mental-imagery.htm (accessed October 22, 2010).

Park, Alice. "Staying Sharp: Getting and Staying in the Zone." *Time.com: Breaking News, Analysis, Politics, Blogs, News Photos, Video, Tech Reviews.* June 8, 2006. http://www.time.com/time/magazine/article/0,9171,1147173,00.html (accessed March 9, 2011).

Plessinger, Annie. "Mental Imagery." *Vanderbilt University: Nashville, Tennessee.* http://www.vanderbilt.edu/ans/psychology/health_psychology/mentalimagery.html (accessed October 22, 2010).

Purdue University. "Good Golf Players See The Hole As Larger Than Poor Players." *ScienceDaily.* July 8, 2008. http://www.sciencedaily.com /releases/2008/07/080707161405.htm (accessed October 22, 2010).

Sideroff, Stephen. "The "Mind-set" of an Olympic Athlete - Training Zone Articles." *MakeItPro™: A Global Sports Social Network - Your Destination & Resource Center for Everything Sports!* February 11, 2010. http://www.makeitpro.com/people/experts/82/articles/show/80 (accessed October 22, 2010).

Smith, D. "What Happens When Athletes Buckle under Pressure?" *Monitor On Psychology* 33.2 (2002): 15.

**Chapter 9: Lifestyle Choices for Athletic Eyes**

Bergin, Cheryl L. "Use Nutrition as a Tool for Managing

Ocular Disease." *Primary Care Optometry News* 14.8 (August 2009): 10-19.

Cover-Miller, Denise N. "Carefully Designed Oral Nutritional Supplements Can Benefit All Patients." *Primary Care Optometry News* (October 2010): 1+.

Semes, Leo, and Diana Shechtman. "'Newtrition.' An Update on Dietary Supplements for AMD." *Review of Optometry* 147.6 (2010): 95-103.

Vyas, Darshna D., and Pinakin Gunvant. "Nutritional Therapeutics for the Eye." *Review of Optometry* 146.10 (2009): 29-34.

**Chapter 10: Eye Injuries**

Branecky, Paul. "Stiched-up Ruutu Still A Happy Cane." February 27, 2008. http://hurricanes.nhl.com/club/news.htm?id=471317 (accessed March 14, 2011).

Ciuffreda, Kenneth J., Daniella Rutner, Neera Kapoor, Irwin Suchoff, Shoshana Craig, and M.E. Han. "Vision Therapy for Oculomotor Dysfunctions in Acquired Brain Injury: A Retrospective Analysis." *Optometry* 79.1 (2008): 18-22.

Decock, Luck. "Cullen's Focus Isn't Lost." *News and Observer.* February 2, 2008.

Karnath, H.O., E. Reich, C. Rorden, M. Fetter, and J. Driver, "The perception of body orientation after neck-proprioceptive stimulation: effects of time and of visual cueing." *Experimental Brain Research* 143.3 (2001): 350–358.

Knox, Richard. "Hockey Puck Test Helps Detect Concussions." *National Public Radio News & Analysis, World,*

*US, Music & Arts.* February 16, 2010.
http://www.npr.org/templates/story/story.
php?storyId=123761643 (accessed March 14, 2011).

Neurotrauma Registry. "Midline Shift Visual Problems after Brain Injury." *Individuals Who Have Acquired Brain Injury (ABI), Spinal Cord Injury (SCI).* 2004.
http://www.neure.com/Index.cfm?file=midlinevisionshift.htm (accessed October 22, 2010).

Yerdon, Joe. "Bob Probert Discovered to Have Had Degenerative Brain Disease." *ProHockeyTalk.* March 3, 2011
http://prohockeytalk.nbcsports.com/2011/03/03/bob-probert-discovered-to-have-degenerative-brain-disease/ (accessed March 9, 2011).

# ABOUT THE AUTHOR

Dr. Michael Peters is a practicing partner of Eye Care Associates, based in Raleigh, NC, which currently is the twentieth-largest provider of eye care in the United States with 30 doctors and 20 offices. He attended West Virginia University for his undergraduate work and received his doctorate from the Pennsylvania College of Optometry in 1988. After graduation, he started his sports-vision specialty at Eye Care Associates and is currently the director of their sports-vision program. He is the eye doctor for several area professional sports teams and continues to work with elite athletes and athletes in the Olympic, collegiate, and amateur ranks. He has also lectured and published articles nationally on his work with athletes. He lives in Raleigh with his wife, Stacey, and their three daughters.